6
SECRETS
to a
LASTING
LOVE

DR. GARY & BARBARA
ROSBERG

LifeWay Press®
Nashville, Tennessee

Published by LifeWay Press®
© 2008 Gary and Barb Rosberg

ISBN 978-1-4158-6565-1
Item 005154527

This book is the resource for course CG-1420 in the subject heading
Personal Life in the Christian Growth Study Plan.

Dewey decimal classification: 306.872
Subject headings: MARRIAGE \ LOVE

To order additional copies of this resource, write LifeWay Church Resources
Customer Service; One LifeWay Plaza; Nashville, TN 37234-0013;
fax (615) 251-5933; call toll free (800) 458-2772; order online at *www.lifeway.com;*
e-mail *orderentry@lifeway.com;* or visit the LifeWay Christian Store serving you.

Printed in the United States of America

Leadership and Adult Publishing
LifeWay Church Resources
One LifeWay Plaza
Nashville, TN 37234-0175

CONTENTS

MEET YOUR COACHES

Dr. Gary and Barbara Rosberg host a popular, nationally syndicated radio program called "Dr. Gary and Barb Rosberg—Your Marriage Coaches." Award-winning authors and marriage-conference speakers, the Rosbergs have written more than a dozen prominent marriage and family resources, including *6 Secrets to a Lasting Love, 40 Unforgettable Dates with Your Mate,* and *The 5 Sex Needs of Men and Women* (see p. 112).

Gary, who earned his EdD from Drake University, has been a marriage and family counselor for more than 25 years. Barb earned her BFA from Drake University and is a sought-after speaker for women's groups and other ministries.

For more information on the Rosbergs' ministry, call (888) 608-COACH or visit *www.drgaryandbarb.com.*

PREVIEW
THE GAME PLAN

THE GREAT MARRIAGE EXPERIENCE

With life's distractions many couples find it hard to intentionally focus on the things that matter most to keep their marriages fresh, vibrant, and growing stronger, regardless of their circumstances. A practical process is needed, with resources that build on one another to affirm this kind of relationship, no matter what stage of marriage a couple is in.

The Rosbergs have created The Great Marriage Experience to provide that kind of ongoing biblical process. The Great Marriage Experience is a road map that equips couples to unlock, discover, and live 6 secrets to a lasting love—secrets to experience a great marriage for a lifetime.

This *6 Secrets to a Lasting Love* DVD study provides an introductory overview of all 6 secrets and is a great place to start The Great Marriage Experience.

ELEMENTS OF THE GREAT MARRIAGE EXPERIENCE

Unlock the secrets. "Where are we in our marriage relationship?" Through the Rosberg Marital Assessment Program (R-MAP), learn where the greatest strengths and growth opportunities are in your marriage, as well as practical first steps to make your marriage great. During this study you will examine your marriage, using the Marriage Map introduced in session 1. Together with your spouse, you will identify where you are in your relationship and set your sights on developing a great marriage. Your small group will help along the journey.

Discover the secrets. "What can give our marriage more depth? Go deeper by applying the secrets to a lasting love through a progression of in-depth resources and conferences for couples, churches, and small groups. This first DVD study is just the beginning—an initial overview of all 6 secrets. After this study you can continue growing, based on your interests and needs, through resources available on each individual secret. (See p. 112 and "Optional Next-Level Reading" assignments that follow each session.)

Live the secrets. "How do we keep focusing on our marriage in spite of life's constant distractions?" A great marriage is built and reinforced over time. If you would like to be a member of The Great Marriage Experience, the Rosbergs will regularly coach and encourage you with hot marriage topics that will keep your attention on what matters most. Go to *www.thegreatmarriageexperience.com* for details. You can also receive daily encouragement through Gary & Barb's national radio program and podcasts, available online.

Churches. Is your church interested in a marriage-ministry approach that develops, reinforces, and replicates a culture of great, godly marriages in your church? Check out The Great Marriage Experience for churches at *www.thegreatmarriageexperience.com*.

STUDYING 6 SECRETS

This DVD study of *6 Secrets to a Lasting Love* will introduce you to six kinds of love that will enrich and strengthen your marriage. Though you can work through this study as a couple, you will gain more by studying these secrets together with a small group of other couples. Together you will be able to help one another better understand the secrets and apply them to common life situations couples face.

TIME AND PLACE

Some groups may choose to meet at church during regularly scheduled program times. This option may meet your child-care needs. However, others will choose to meet in a home, an apartment, or a community room, where informal relationships can be fostered. Select a time when you can devote at least 75 minutes to each session. Allowing additional time for more discussion and informal fellowship will enhance your experience together. You will need at least seven weekly sessions to complete the study.

HOST COUPLE AND LEADER

If your group meets in a home or in another informal setting, a host couple can provide for an environment conducive to a group experience. You'll need a TV and DVD player. The hosts can provide coffee or soft drinks and light refreshments, or couples can take turns supplying these for the group. A small-group leader will guide the sessions, using this member book. Suggestions for the leader are found on page 110, and the sharing and discussion suggestions are provided in the sessions for everyone to follow. If your group prefers, you could rotate leadership of the sessions.

RESOURCES

Each couple will need at least one member book, although some couples may prefer to have a book for each spouse. The group will need one leader kit, which includes the DVD messages by Gary and Barbara Rosberg. It also includes a review copy of *6 Secrets to a Lasting Love* trade book by Tyndale House Publishers. This book is recommended but not required for this study. At the end of each session, chapters in the trade book are recommended for taking your understanding and experience of a particular secret to the next level. The LifeWay member book and leader kit are available by calling toll free (800) 458-2772; by ordering online at *www.lifeway.com;* or by visiting the LifeWay Christian Store serving you. The trade book and additional resources by the Rosbergs are listed with ordering information on page 112.

COMPONENTS OF EACH SESSION

Each session is designed for at least 75 minutes. The session plans recommend times for each segment of the session. Each session includes the following elements.

REVEALING

1. *Warm-Ups.* Each session opens with Scripture and talking to God. Then you will take time to build your relationships with group members, using team-building activities.
2. *Instant Replay.* Each session includes a time to review the previous session's content and to share insights you may have gained from your experiences and application of the secrets during the week.
3. *Coaches' Comments.* Gary and Barb will be your marriage coaches for this marriage experience. You will listen to the DVD messages and use the listening guide to take notes.
4. *Turn to Your Mate.* This brief activity will guide you and your spouse to talk to each other about the DVD message you will have heard.
5. *Discussing the DVD Message.* These questions will guide your group to discuss the insights from Gary and Barb's DVD message.

UNDERSTANDING

Questions and activities will guide you to a deeper understanding of each secret. You will examine Scriptures that relate to the secret and discuss their applications. You will identify and discuss examples of behaviors that would characterize the kind of love you are studying, and you will also look at behaviors that are contrary to that expression of love.

APPLYING

Case studies will give your group an opportunity to talk about the application of what you're learning to real-life situations. By examining common experiences couples face in their marriages, you can give and receive *anonymous* counsel for issues you may face in your own marriage. You will also be prepared if those issues arise in the future.

BRINGING IT HOME

This DVD study of the 6 secrets does not include much work outside the small-group session. In "Bringing It Home" you will be asked to take your mate on a date; but that's not work, is it? You will take time after session 1 to locate your marriage on the Marriage Map. Session 2 will introduce you to closing the loop on unresolved conflicts in your relationship. Closing the loop may take some time, but the results of healed relationships will be well worth the effort.

Optional Next-Level Reading. One final segment following each session will list additional resources from the Rosbergs that will help you go deeper in your understanding and application of each secret. If you recognize that you need more help in a particular area, check out these books.

OUR 6 SECRETS JOURNAL

The next seven weeks will include challenges and adventures as you assess your marriage relationship, remember your dreams, go on some interesting dates, and experiment with new dimensions of loving each other. Keep a journal (or a scrapbook if you prefer) of your experiences. Along the way we'll recommend some things for you to add to your journal. These things aren't limited to words. You may want to include notes, photos, or other mementos of your experiences. Make some memories and record them!

OK, let's get into the game. Huddle up!

PURSUING YOUR DREAM MARRIAGE

HEBREWS 13:4, NIV

MARRIAGE SHOULD BE HONORED BY ALL,
AND THE MARRIAGE BED KEPT PURE.

Revealing
PURSUING YOUR DREAM MARRIAGE

WARM-UPS
(15 MINUTES)

Read Hebrews 13:4 and begin your study by asking God to reveal to each person His secrets for the kind of love that will help your marriage last. Invite Him to mold and shape your relationships during the coming weeks.

TEAM BUILDING

As a couple, introduce yourselves to the group. Take turns sharing the following.

- Your names
- How long you've been married
- Names and ages of your children and/or family pets
- How you first met
- Your first date or one of your most memorable dates

PREVIEW THE GAME PLAN
(5 MINUTES)

LEADER: Invite members to scan through their books to identify the various elements. Encourage them to read "Preview the Game Plan" (pp. 5–8) if they have not already done so.

Review the key elements of your group study of *6 Secrets to a Lasting Love*, described on pages 7–8.

1. Revealing (for example, pp. 22–26)

2. Understanding (for example, pp. 27–31)

3. Applying (for example, pp. 32–33)

4. Bringing It Home (for example, p. 34)

GROUP COVENANT
(5 MINUTES)

Read the agreements we're asking you to make and check your responses in the margin.

Will you commit to this?

1. CONCENTRATE ON YOUR SPOUSE'S NEEDS

Take the responsibility to give to your spouse and trust that God will meet your own needs in whatever way He chooses. By being other-focused and concerned about meeting your spouse's needs first, you may be surprised how God blesses you by involving your spouse in meeting each of your own needs.

❏ Yes ❏ No
❏ Does this mean it's not going to be all about me anymore?

2. AVOID CRITICISM

When it's time for your spouse to focus on your needs, be careful not to criticize the way he or she hasn't met your past needs. Express how you personally feel without making accusations. Never criticize your spouse to the group.

❏ Yes ❏ No
❏ What happens if I don't avoid it?

3. KEEP YOUR GROUP SHARING TIME SAFE

Some, if not all, in your group will want to share the progress that each person is making from week to week. Keep your sharing time confidential within your group and avoid comparing each other's marriage relationships. Make your group a safe place to share your strengths and struggles.

❏ Yes ❏ No
❏ Does this mean I can't secretly record our group meetings?

4. FOCUS ON BEING AS WELL AS DOING

Meeting your spouse's needs involves doing something. But your doing is empowered by being something. As your attitudes are transformed, your behavior changes. So throughout this course you will be asked to focus on certain Christlike attitudes that will direct your actions. Will you ask God to help you change in attitude and action?

❏ Yes ❏ No
❏ I didn't know I needed to change.

5. COMPLETE YOUR HOME ASSIGNMENTS

You will be asked to take your mate on a date between sessions each week. Occasionally, you will be asked to complete an additional assignment that is more appropriately done in private with your spouse. Will you commit to a weekly date with your mate and these extra activities to pursue your dream marriage?

❏ Yes ❏ No
❏ Will I get paid?

COACHES' COMMENTS
DVD SESSION 1 (18 MINUTES)

Scripture

Hebrews 13:4

Biblical _____ is at risk.

God's got the _____ for marriage.

Your marriage is the front line of _____.

Great marriages don't just happen. We have to be
_____ to have a great marriage.

SIX SECRETS TO A LASTING LOVE

_____ love

_____ love

_____ love

_____ love

_____ love

_____ love

MARRIAGE MAP

In case you missed a word during the DVD ...

marriage, answer, ministry, intentional, Forgiving, Serving, Persevering, Guarding, Celebrating, Renewing, disappointment, discouragement, distance, disconnect, discord, divorce

From dream to _____

From disappointment to _____

From discouragement to _____

From distance to _____

From disconnect to _____

From discord to emotional _____

12

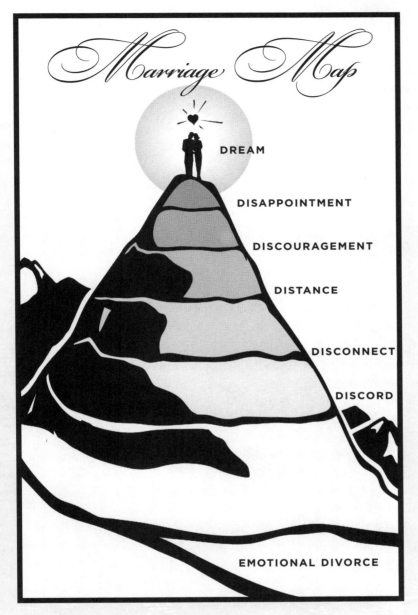

Marriage Map

DREAM

DISAPPOINTMENT

DISCOURAGEMENT

DISTANCE

DISCONNECT

DISCORD

EMOTIONAL DIVORCE

 # TURN TO YOUR MATE
(7 MINUTES)

Turn to your mate and talk about which of the six secrets you are <u>most</u> eager to develop more deeply in your marriage. Describe for each other one dream about your marriage that you would like to revive. (We'll help you work on the Marriage Map assessment at home this week.)

**LEADER:
For privacy play some instrumental background music so that couples will not fear being overheard.**

DISCUSSING THE DVD MESSAGE
(10 MINUTES)

1. What are some of the chief reasons marriages are at risk today?

2. Why do you think achieving great marriages requires intentionality?

3. Below is a list of six saboteurs that can undermine the joy in your marriage and cool your feelings of love for each other. As a group, match the type of love in the margin with the saboteur it can overcome.

6 Secrets

1. Forgiving Love

2. Serving Love

3. Persevering Love

4. Guarding Love

5. Celebrating Love

6. Renewing Love

_____ a. Same ol' same ol'—stuck hearts

_____ b. Walk-away wives and husbands—giving-up hearts

_____ c. I-centered—selfish hearts

_____ d. Refusing to resolve conflict—hard hearts

_____ e. Lack of joy—isolated hearts

_____ f. Giving in to temptations—unguarded hearts

4. We're going to guide you to find your place on the Marriage Map this week. Why do you think knowing your place on the map will help you begin taking intentional steps to pursue your dream marriage?

Understanding

PURSUING YOUR DREAM MARRIAGE

(10 MINUTES)

Let's start at the beginning. Read how God created the first marriage, described in Genesis 2:15-25.

"The LORD God placed the man in the Garden of Eden to tend and care for it …

"The LORD God said, 'It is not good for the man to be alone. I will make a companion who will help him.' So the LORD God formed from the soil every kind of animal and bird. He brought them to Adam to see what he would call them, and Adam chose a name for each one. He gave names to all the livestock, birds, and wild animals. But still there was no companion suitable for him. So the LORD God caused Adam to fall into a deep sleep. He took one of Adam's ribs and closed up the place from which he had taken it. Then the LORD God made a woman from the rib and brought her to Adam.

" 'At last!' Adam exclaimed. 'She is part of my own flesh and bone! She will be called 'woman,' because she was taken out of a man.' This explains why a man leaves his father and mother and is joined to his wife, and the two are united into one. Now, although Adam and his wife were both naked, neither of them felt any shame."
GENESIS 2:15,18-25

1. Try to put yourself in Adam's place when Eve showed up. What do you think he was feeling and thinking when he said, "At last!"? How would you paraphrase his response?

2. Because God designed marriage, He has a plan for your marriage. Why did He institute marriage in the first place? Check all that apply. Then discuss your answers.
   - ❐ To remove human aloneness
   - ❐ To frustrate human beings
   - ❐ To encourage human beings
   - ❐ To make life perfect
   - ❐ To make life difficult
   - ❐ To give Adam something to do
   - ❐ To populate the earth
   - ❐ To meet emotional needs
   - ❐ To provide companionship
   - ❐ Others:

3. In God's plan for marriage, the husband and the wife have a relationship characterized by the words listed below. Check the boxes beside words that describe your relationship. Circle the words that describe areas in which you would like to see improvement.
   - ❐ Loving
   - ❐ Compatible
   - ❐ Happy
   - ❐ Permanent
   - ❐ Companions
   - ❐ United in purpose
   - ❐ Emotionally intimate
   - ❐ Emotionally healthy
   - ❐ Growing closer
   - ❐ Content
   - ❐ Spiritually intimate
   - ❐ Honest about faults

4. What other words would you use to describe God's plan for marriage? Brainstorm and make a list here.

5. God sent the following message to the exiles of Judah while they were in captivity in Babylon.

" 'I know the plans I have for you,' says the LORD. 'They are plans for good and not for disaster, to give you a future and a hope. In those days when you pray, I will listen. If you look for me in earnest, you will find me when you seek me. I will be found by you,' says the LORD. 'I will end your captivity and restore your fortunes.' "
JEREMIAH 29:11-14

Do you really believe God's plans for you and your marriage are "plans for good and not for disaster, to give you a future and a hope"? Explain.

Ask a volunteer to pray that God will speak Jeremiah 29:11 over your marriages. Ask God to give each of you a renewed sense of hope for the future and to draw you as couples to Himself and into the marriages for which you yearn.

Applying

PURSUING YOUR DREAM MARRIAGE

CASE STUDY 1

Jerry and Susan

Jerry and Susan have been married 25 years. Their nest is empty now. Both have demanding professional careers but very little in common that draws them together. They would say the fire is gone from their marriage. They seldom talk and often spend their free time in activities without their mate.

CASE STUDY 2

Isaiah and Elizabeth

Isaiah and Elizabeth just celebrated their second anniversary. In many respects they still act like newlyweds. But Elizabeth has been making a mental list of things she wants to help Isaiah change. He's been wounded several times when he's overheard her talking to her mom about his flaws. He concludes, "She's not perfect either."

CORRESPONDENCE

CASE STUDY 3

Ann and Coty

Ann and Coty both grew up in the homes of alcoholics. Although they don't drink, the anger, rage, and verbal abuse (which sometimes gets physical) feel a lot like their childhood homes. Neighbors and friends wonder why and how they can stay together.

CASE STUDIES
DISCUSS ONE OR TWO CASE STUDIES (5 MINUTES)

You'll learn more this week about the Marriage Map, and we'll help you find where your marriage is on the map. For now read the case studies on the previous page and discuss the stop at which you think each couple will find their marriage. Give it your best guess.

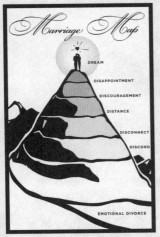

STOPS ON THE MARRIAGE MAP

The Dream Stop
The Disappointment Stop
The Discouragement Stop
The Distance Stop
The Disconnect Stop
The Discord Stop
The Emotional-Divorce Stop

TURNING TOWARD HOME

Before next week's session use the assessment on pages 95–100 to determine where your marriage is on the map.

Optional take-home assignment: Remember the picture Sarah drew for Gary? If you have children, ask them to draw pictures of your family. Then invite them to interpret their pictures. See whether their pictures and interpretations have anything to say to you about the status of your marriage. Maybe you'll frame your kids' pictures too.

During a time of silent prayer, ask God to help you and your spouse be intentional about pursuing your desires for your marriage.

Bringing It Home

DATE YOUR MATE

Choose one of the following suggestions and take your mate on a date. After your date, pray together and thank God for your marriage. Invite God to guide your marriage relationship so that you will experience all the best He desires for you. Add a memento, picture, receipt, and/or a journal entry to *Our 6 Secrets Journal* (see p. 8).

1. Arrange for a night at home alone to recall the dreams you had when you first got married. Order Chinese food or another favorite for dinner. Review your wedding pictures. Watch a video or or listen to a CD or an audiotape of your ceremony. Share with your spouse the qualities that attracted you to him or her. Recall your big dreams for your life together.

2. Husbands, try to recall your first date (or at least an early one). Plan a similar date or go to a romantic place that reminds you of your dating days. Share with each other the qualities that attracted you to him or her. Recall your big dreams for your life together.

PREPARING FOR SESSION 2

Select and bring to the next small-group session one of your favorite wedding pictures or mementos and be prepared to describe a funny or memorable experience that occurred on your wedding day, during the preparations for the wedding, or on your honeymoon.

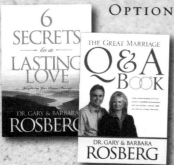

OPTIONAL NEXT-LEVEL READING

Take your understanding of forgiving love to the next level by reading some or all of the following.

6 Secrets to a Lasting Love (Tyndale, 2006)
Chapter 1: When Our Dream Marriage Began to Fade
Chapter 2: Where Are You Headed?

The Great Marriage Q & A Book (Tyndale, 2006)

SECRET ONE
FORGIVING LOVE

Forgiving love heals hurts and helps
spouses feel accepted and connected.
You move from a hard heart
to forgiving love.

COLOSSIANS 3:13
MAKE ALLOWANCE FOR EACH OTHER'S FAULTS AND FORGIVE
THE PERSON WHO OFFENDS YOU. REMEMBER, THE LORD
FORGAVE YOU, SO YOU MUST FORGIVE OTHERS.

Revealing

SECRET ONE • FORGIVING LOVE

WARM-UPS
(10 MINUTES)

Read Colossians 3:13 and pray that God will help you understand and experience the acceptance and connectedness that come from living forgiving love in your marriages.

TEAM BUILDING
Each couple: Display one of your favorite wedding pictures or mementos and briefly describe a funny or memorable experience that occurred on your wedding day, during wedding preparations, or during your honeymoon.

INSTANT REPLAY
(5 MINUTES)

1. What did you hear or process this past week regarding "Pursuing Your Dream Marriage" that hit home or had the greatest impact? Explain.

In Quads

2. Is there an aspect of your dream marriage you wish you could recapture? Describe.

3. Which of the 6 secrets to a lasting love grips your heart most and why?

❐ Secret One, forgiving love, heals the hurts and helps spouses feel accepted and connected.

❐ Secret Two, serving love, discovers and meets needs and helps spouses feel honored and understood.

❐ Secret Three, persevering love, stays strong in tough times and helps spouses feel bonded, best friends for life.

❐ Secret Four, guarding love, protects from threats and helps spouses feel safe and secure.

❐ Secret Five, celebrating love, rejoices in the marriage relationship and helps spouses feel cherished and captivated.

❐ Secret Six, renewing love, refreshes and supports the marriage bond and helps spouses feel confident and rooted.

LEADER: Depending on what is shared, you may want to stop and pray for one another or thank the Lord for what He's been doing in your marriages.

COACHES' COMMENTS
DVD SESSION 2 (22 MINUTES)

Scriptures

2 Chronicles 7:14

James 5:16

Revelation 3:20

If you _____, He will speak.

When we have restoration with _____,
it moves us to have restoration with our mates.

Marriage can handle _____, but it cannot handle deception.

Conflict starts with an _____.

An offense leads to an emotional response—_____.

When my heart is _____, I'm hard toward God.

If we don't deal with the hurt, it becomes _____.

When we have unforgiveness in our relationship, we break
fellowship with the _____.

He will give you a spirit of _____.

FOUR PARTS OF FORGIVENESS
(Step 4 in "Closing the Loop")

• CONFESSION: "I am wrong."

**In case you
missed a word
during the DVD ...**

listen, God, sin, offense,
hurt, hard, anger, Holy
Spirit, humility, Sorrow,
Request, past

• _____: "I'm sorry for what I did."

• REPENTANCE: "I don't ever want to hurt you again."

• _____: "Will you forgive me?"

Forgiveness releases the _____.

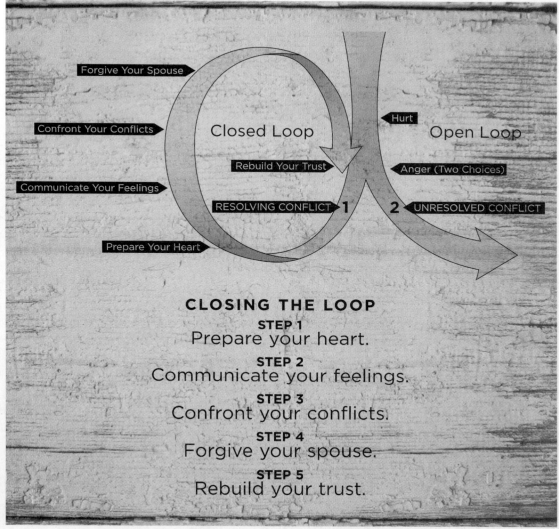

Forgive Your Spouse

Confront Your Conflicts

Closed Loop

Hurt

Open Loop

Rebuild Your Trust

Anger (Two Choices)

Communicate Your Feelings

RESOLVING CONFLICT 1

2 UNRESOLVED CONFLICT

Prepare Your Heart

CLOSING THE LOOP

STEP 1
Prepare your heart.

STEP 2
Communicate your feelings.

STEP 3
Confront your conflicts.

STEP 4
Forgive your spouse.

STEP 5
Rebuild your trust.

For more details on closing the loop, see pages 101-3.

TURN TO YOUR MATE
(5 MINUTES)

Turn to your mate and take turns identifying and sharing about any unresolved offenses in your relationship. Agree to learn more about closing the loop on those areas during the coming week. You will get more help on closing the loop.

LEADER:
For privacy play some instrumental background music so that couples will not fear being overheard.

DISCUSSING THE DVD MESSAGE

(5 MINUTES)

In Quads

LEADER: Begin with a two-minute review of the open and closed loops mentioned in the DVD message and illustrated on the previous page. Remind members they will use this process during the week. (For more details on closing the loop, see pp. 101–3.)

1. What did Gary or Barb share during the DVD message that was particularly insightful or instructive? Discuss.

2. How do you think this radical kind of forgiving love could impact your marriage environment/experience?

Understanding
SECRET ONE ● FORGIVING LOVE
(13 MINUTES)

As a Group

1. As you read the following Scriptures, list below or in the margin ways God has demonstrated a kind of forgiving love toward us.

> "He has removed our rebellious acts as far away from us as the east is from the west."
> **PSALM 103:12**

> "He has rescued us from the one who rules in the kingdom of darkness, and he has brought us into the Kingdom of his dear Son. God has purchased our freedom with his blood and has forgiven all our sins. Now he has brought you back as his friends. He has done this through his death on the cross in his own human body. As a result, he has brought you into the very presence of God, and you are holy and blameless as you stand before him without a single fault."
> **COLOSSIANS 1:13-14,22**

> "If we confess our sins to him, he is faithful and just to forgive us and to cleanse us from every wrong."
> **1 JOHN 1:9**

Forgiving Love

Forgiving love offers a fresh start after you have offended and hurt each other. Forgiving love equips you to communicate on such a deep level of acceptance for one another that you can recover from the pain you occasionally inflict on one another and work through your offenses. Forgiving love helps you to reconnect after you have hurt one another.

God's Model of Forgiveness

Ask volunteers to read Jesus' statements below.

Note: Jesus wants us to live with a spirit of forgiveness, no matter how frequent the offenses; however, this is not a license for abuse. If you are living in an abusive relationship, consider seeking professional counseling. Ask your pastor or another trusted Christian leader to recommend a counselor.

"Peter came to him and asked, 'Lord, how often should I forgive someone who sins against me? Seven times?'
    "'No!' Jesus replied, 'seventy times seven!'"
MATTHEW 18:21-22

"If another believer sins, rebuke him; then if he repents, forgive him. Even if he wrongs you seven times a day and each time turns again and asks forgiveness, forgive him."
LUKE 17:3-4

2. Why do you think these would be considered hard sayings of Jesus? What makes them so hard to follow?

"If you are standing before the altar in the Temple, offering a sacrifice to God, and you suddenly remember that someone has something against you, leave your sacrifice there beside the altar. Go and be reconciled to that person. Then come and offer your sacrifice to God."
MATTHEW 5:23-24

3. Why do you think Jesus said such a shocking thing—that you should interrupt your worship to get things right with others?

4. If you applied Jesus' teaching to your marriage, what difference (if any) would it make in your relationship with your spouse and why?

How might it affect your worship experience? Explain.

"If you forgive those who sin against you,
your heavenly Father will forgive you.
But if you refuse to forgive others,
your Father will not forgive your sins."
MATTHEW 6:14-15

5. God seems so intent on our living a spirit of forgiving love. According to Matthew 6:14-15, what else is at stake if we don't?

6. Read Philippians 2:1-2 below. What part do tenderness and compassion play in transforming a marriage? Explain.

"If you have any encouragement from being
united with Christ, if any comfort from his love,
if any fellowship with the Spirit, *if any tenderness
and compassion, then make my joy complete*
by being like-minded, having the same love,
being one in spirit and purpose."
PHILIPPIANS 2:1-2, NIV, *emphasis added*

7. Contrast below the differences between a person who may struggle with or be stuck in unforgiveness and one who is characterized by tenderness, compassion, and a forgiving spirit. Classify the examples in the margin and then make your own list. Take turns around the group listing characteristics or common behaviors of each.

Stuck in Unforgiveness   Tender/Forgiving

Examples

1. Choosing not to hold the offense against your spouse even before he or she asks for forgiveness

2. Keeping a list of wrongs as ammunition for the next argument

3. Waiting to forgive until your spouse confesses the wrong and asks for forgiveness

4. Accepting forgiveness but being patient when your spouse needs time for trust to be restored or hurts to be healed

8. Which approach was most common in the family system in which you were reared?

For more examples see page 104.

9. In the light of Jesus' teachings, what changes would you like to make in your behavior with His help?

FORGIVENESS MYTHS

Read the following forgiveness myths and discuss the question that follows.

MYTH 1: "When I forgive, I must also forget."

MYTH 2: "The hurt is too great. It is impossible for me to forgive."

MYTH 3: "I don't feel like forgiving, so my forgiveness can't be genuine."

MYTH 4: "I can't forgive until the other person asks for it."

MYTH 5: "In order to forgive, I must pretend that nothing bad happened."

MYTH 6: "I must forgive right away, or it doesn't count."

In Quads
(5 MINUTES)

Note: If you struggle with understanding why a myth is wrong, see the explanation in the *6 Secrets* book (pp. 54–57), listed in "Optional Next-Level Reading."

Which one of these forgiveness myths has most hindered your forgiveness in the past? Discuss.

Applying

SECRET ONE • FORGIVING LOVE

CASE STUDY 1
Susan and Andy

Susan spent too much money secretively over several months. This is not the first time. The Holy Spirit is convicting her about this deception. She wants to come clean with Andy but fears his reaction. She's afraid he will not forgive.

CASE STUDY 2
Marshall and Ericka

Marshall is avoiding connecting with his wife and experiencing intimacy. He confesses sexual sin from early in their marriage. Ericka is willing to work through the process of forgiveness, but she lacks trust that he isn't violating emotional intimacy with a woman at his workplace.

CORRESPONDENCE

CASE STUDY 3
Carlos and Maria

Carlos continues to express anger towards his wife and children. Maria distances from him and tries to protect the children. She concludes that they can't reconnect. He moves towards her to break the pattern, explaining God is changing his heart. She is reticent to try again and is considering walking away from the marriage.

DISCUSS ONE OR TWO CASE STUDIES (10 MINUTES)

CASE STUDY 1: SUSAN AND ANDY

Read about Susan and Andy. Divide into groups and discuss the following questions. Then share your responses with the large group.

WIVES: What steps would you recommend for Susan to share this with Andy and begin changing her spending patterns?

HUSBANDS: What behaviors by Andy might be driving or influencing Susan's fear? What things could Andy do to create an environment in which Susan would not be afraid to be honest with Him?

CASE STUDY 2: MARSHALL AND ERICKA

1. What should Marshall do to rebuild Ericka's trust?

2. How should Ericka respond to her concerns about the woman at work?

CASE STUDY 3: CARLOS AND MARIA

Based on what you've learned about forgiving love, how might you counsel Carlos and Maria?

TURNING TOWARD HOME

Take time now to ask God to give each person the desired freedom to live in tenderness and compassion.

Ask God for the wisdom and power to practice forgiving love as He models for us.

Ask God to bring healing to the wounds of the past so that spouses will be strong to live in tenderness and compassion.

Bringing It Home

DATE YOUR MATE

In the business of life, we often avoid dealing with offenses because of the time required. Sometimes, like Barb mentioned in the DVD message, we allow past unresolved conflicts to affect our present. This week we want you to be very intentional about blocking out time to talk about closing the loop wherever it's needed.

Choose one of the following suggestions and take your mate on a date. After your date, add a memento, picture, receipt, and/or journal entry to *Our 6 Secrets Journal*.

1. Plan an overnight getaway. Plan one entertaining activity, but devote the bulk of your time to talking.

2. Go outdoors to a park, a hiking trail, a lake, a mountaintop, or a similar place. Take time to walk, talk, or drive and park (if the weather requires) and enjoy the beauty of God's creation. Take unhindered time to talk.

Begin working on closing the loop to the unresolved conflicts you uncover in your marriage. Pace yourself and take breaks if needed.

1. Read the tips on pages 101–3 or chapter 4 in the optional reading list below.

2. See whether you can identify times in the past when you have closed the loop on offenses. Celebrate those victories.

3. Identify issues that you sense may still be unresolved. Follow the steps to closing the loop.

OPTIONAL NEXT-LEVEL READING

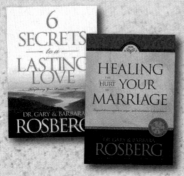

Take your understanding of forgiving love to the next level by reading some or all of the following.

6 Secrets to a Lasting Love (Tyndale, 2006)
Chapter 3: The Rocky Road of Hurt and Anger
Chapter 4: Closing the Loop

Healing the Hurt in Your Marriage (Tyndale, 2004)

SECRET TWO
SERVING LOVE

Serving love discovers and meets needs and
helps spouses feel honored and understood.
You move from selfish hearts to serving love.

ROMANS 12:10, NIV
HONOR ONE ANOTHER ABOVE YOURSELVES.

Revealing

SECRET TWO • SERVING LOVE

WARM-UPS
(10 MINUTES)

Read Romans 12:10 and ask God to develop in each husband and wife a spirit of serving love that will cause their spouses to feel honored and understood.

TEAM BUILDING

Consider the places you go where you receive service, such as a restaurant, an auto-repair shop, the dry cleaner, and the grocery store. What defines good service in these areas? What are some of your pet peeves regarding bad service?

Describe one experience in which you received service far beyond what was expected.

INSTANT REPLAY
(7 MINUTES)

1. What have you heard or processed about forgiving love that hit home or had the greatest impact? Explain.

Review the steps to closing the loop.

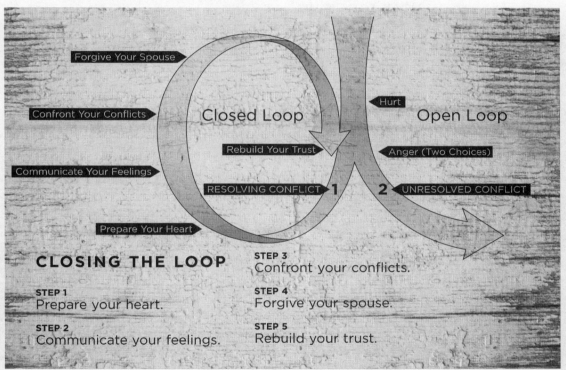

Forgive Your Spouse

Confront Your Conflicts

Communicate Your Feelings

Prepare Your Heart

Closed Loop

Rebuild Your Trust

RESOLVING CONFLICT 1

Hurt

Open Loop

Anger (Two Choices)

2 UNRESOLVED CONFLICT

CLOSING THE LOOP

STEP 1
Prepare your heart.

STEP 2
Communicate your feelings.

STEP 3
Confront your conflicts.

STEP 4
Forgive your spouse.

STEP 5
Rebuild your trust.

2. While using "Closing the Loop" this week, did you learn or experience anything about the process of forgiveness that brought healing, reconciliation, or perhaps a breakthrough in your marriage relationship?

LEADER: Depending on what is shared, you may want to stop and pray for one another or thank the Lord for what He's been doing in your marriages.

COACHES' COMMENTS
DVD SESSION 3 (23 MINUTES)

Scriptures

John 13:12-17

Philippians 2:1-3

Ephesians 5:25-32

Jesus wants us to _____ one another.

I was missing the spirit of _____.

We tend to exercise our _____ ... [and] pride.

WHY DON'T WE SERVE?
1. Maybe you didn't see it in the family you grew up in.
2. _____ or selfishness
3. Don't know how to lower ourselves

50/50 relationship—_____ spirit

Interdependent spirit—two people focused on Christ

God's way is a _____ percent outserving each other.

RESULTS OF SERVING
1. I feel _____ and esteemed.
2. I'm getting the overflow of his relationship with Jesus.
3. It opens _____ between us.

IDEAS FOR HUSBANDS
1. Ask your wife how you can practically lighten her _____.
2. Take 20 minutes a day for connection time.

In case you missed a word during the DVD ...

serve, humility, selfishness, Pride, independent, 100/100, honored, communication, load, priority, curious, other

IDEAS FOR WIVES
1. Make time alone with him a _____.
2. Affirm your husband's maleness.
3. Be more _____ than critical.
4. Tell him what you need.

We become _____-centered.

TURN TO YOUR MATE
(5 MINUTES)

Turn to your mate and ask for two or three suggestions on how you can serve him or her this week. Find out how you can lighten the load, relieve the stress, support, or encourage through acts of serving love.

LEADER:
For privacy play some instrumental background music so that couples will not fear being overheard.

DISCUSSING THE DVD MESSAGE
(5 MINUTES)

1. What do you think about Gary and Barb's description of a marriage characterized by serving love?
   - With which aspects do you agree?
   - What would you be most eager to experience?
   - To what parts, if any, do you have difficulty relating?

2. Gary and Barb talk about marriage not being a 50/50 concept. Instead, it should be 100/100—that is, each spouse gives 100 percent to the marriage. What do you think a 100/100 marriage would look like? Why do you think the 100/100 concept is vital for a healthy marriage?

3. Did Gary or Barb share anything during the DVD message that was particularly insightful or instructive? If so, discuss.

Understanding

SECRET TWO • SERVING LOVE
(15 MINUTES)

Serving Love

Serving love helps you discover and meet each other's deepest needs. Serving love is the process of identifying needs and taking steps to meet them in each other.

Read about Jesus washing the disciples' feet and answer the questions that follow.

"Jesus knew that the Father had given him authority over everything and that he had come from God and would return to God. So he got up from the table, took off his robe, wrapped a towel around his waist, and poured water into a basin. Then he began to wash the disciples' feet and to wipe them with the towel he had around him.

"After washing their feet, he put on his robe again and sat down and asked, 'Do you understand what I was doing? You call me "Teacher" and "Lord," and you are right, because it is true. And since I, the Lord and Teacher, have washed your feet, you ought to wash each other's feet. I have given you an example to follow. Do as I have done to you. How true it is that a servant is not greater than the master. Nor are messengers more important than the one who sends them. You know these things—now do them! That is the path of blessing.' "
JOHN 13:3-5,12-17

1. Jesus demonstrated the heart of a servant. How do you think the disciples felt? What do you imagine was going through their minds?

2. In what ways can we practice Jesus' kind of serving love with our spouses?

3. How could having this attitude revolutionize our marriages? What would the benefits be?

4. Do you have any marriage mentors or heroes? If so, how would you describe their relationship?

5. Read Jesus' instructions from Mark 10:42-45 in the margin. Then contrast below the differences between a person who wants to be served and one who serves others. Classify the examples in the margin and then make your own list. Take a few minutes as a group to list characteristics or common behaviors of each.

Desires to Be Served   Is Willing to Serve Others

6. In the light of Mark 10:42-45, are there any changes in the way you relate to your mate that you need Jesus' help with? If so, what?

Mark 10:42-45

"Jesus called them together and said, 'You know that in this world kings are tyrants, and officials lord it over the people beneath them. But among you it should be quite different. Whoever wants to be a leader among you must be your servant, and whoever wants to be first must be the slave of all. For even I, the Son of Man, came here not to be served but to serve others, and to give my life as a ransom for many.' "

Examples

1. Independent
2. Interdependent
3. Humble
4. Proud
5. Narcissistic
6. Egocentric
7. Demanding
8. Giving
9. Gentle
10. Patient
11. Insistent

As you read Philippians 2:3-8, make a list of words in the margin describing character traits of Christ that could be lived in your marriages.

"Do nothing out of rivalry or conceit, but in humility consider others as more important than yourselves. Everyone should look out not only for his own interests, but also for the interests of others.

"Make your own attitude that of Christ Jesus,

who, existing in the form of God, did not consider equality with God
as something to be used for His own advantage.
Instead He emptied Himself by assuming the form of a slave,
taking on the likeness of men.
And when He had come as a man in His external form,
He humbled Himself by becoming obedient to the point of death—even to death on a cross."
PHILIPPIANS 2:3-8, HCSB

7. How do you feel about trying to integrate these characteristics in your marriage? How might it work or look?

Practicing unselfishness:

Practicing humility:

Showing empathy or concern for the other:

Giving yourself sacrificially:

Read Romans 12:9-10 in the margin.

8. What does it mean to love and honor someone? Share your ideas and record them.

Loving and honoring someone means that I ...

Romans 12:9-10

"Don't just pretend that you love others. Really love them. Hate what is wrong. Stand on the side of the good. Love each other with genuine affection, and take delight in honoring each other."

Individually complete the following self-assessment. Rank the degree to which these characteristics describe your current attitude toward your marriage. Write a number from 1 (low—not my way of thinking) to 5 (high—clearly my way of thinking). Be honest!

_____ a. Meet me halfway.
_____ b. I should get what is rightfully mine.
_____ c. If you love me, I will love you back.
_____ d. When you contribute to this marriage, so will I.
_____ e. I love you just the way you are.
_____ f. I love you because Christ loves me.
_____ g. You do your part, and I'll do mine.
_____ h. I will serve you regardless of how you serve me.
_____ i. I love you in spite of what you do.
_____ j. I want to understand how to meet your needs.
_____ k. My feelings for you are not based on your feelings for me.
_____ l. I choose to forgive you.

9. Review your responses with your spouse and see if he/she agrees with your rating of yourself. Discuss major differences. In light of what you're learning about serving love, which of these would you like to work on changing?

LEADER: If you don't have time for the self-assessment, encourage couples to rate and process their responses at home this week.

As Couples

Applying

SECRET TWO • SERVING LOVE

CASE STUDY 1

Alex and Ramona

Ramona's aging parents are requiring more and more of her time in the caretaking role. Her brothers live out of state. She is choosing to try to care for her parents at the cost of time and focus at home with Alex and her children. Ramona is torn between both areas of love and responsibility.

CASE STUDY 2

Keira and Landon

Keira is distracted from her marriage by filling her life with her children, friendships, work, and church activities. She gains insight when her best friend's husband dies. Keira recommits to connecting to her husband, Landon, by purposing to spend time with him.

CORRESPONDENCE

CASE STUDY 3

Tim and Jade

Tim justifies his long hours and devotion to his job by being an excellent provider for his family's financial needs. He wants emotional support from his wife, Jade. But she can't seem to muster supportive feelings and actions because she feels isolated and disconnected.

DISCUSS ONE OR TWO CASE STUDIES (10 MINUTES)

CASE STUDY 1: ALEX AND RAMONA

1. Describe thoughts, emotions, and conflicts Ramona may be feeling.

2. How can Alex demonstrate his serving love toward Ramona? What can he say and do?

CASE STUDY 2: KEIRA AND LANDON

1. What are some typical ways husbands and wives get distracted from serving one another?

2. Why do you think watching her friend lose her husband caused Keira to recommit to her own relationship with Landon? How might you respond to a similar experience?

CASE STUDY 3: TIM AND JADE

1. Husbands, suppose you are Tim's accountability partners. Based on what you've learned about serving love, what would you recommend that Tim do to restore balance to his life and help Jade feel like giving him the emotional support he needs?

2. Wives, what are some intentional ways Jade could take the first steps to reconnect to Tim and encourage him to move in her direction? What should she avoid doing that might push Tim further away?

TURNING TOWARD HOME

Volunteers, select one or more of these concepts and lead the group in talking to God about your relationships.
- Thank God for your spouse.
- Ask God to soften your heart toward your partner.
- Ask for humility to serve your spouse.
- Ask God to show you how to identify your spouse's needs.
- Ask God to keep those tender emotions close to the surface and to use them to impress on your spouse the sincerity of your love for him or her.

Bringing It Home

DATE YOUR MATE

Choose one of the following suggestions and take your mate on a date. After your date, add a memento, picture, receipt, and/or journal entry to *Our 6 Secrets Journal*.

1. Grab a camera and go on a photo shoot. Select a setting at a park, beach, historic landmark, or another scenic location; in a mall; or around the house and yard. Take turns making candid or just plain goofy photos of each other. Have fun! Ask bystanders to take a few shots of the two of you in crazy poses. Enjoy reviewing your pictures.

2. If job situations allow, meet your spouse for a spontaneous lunch. Pick him or her up at work and go to a restaurant, dine in the company cafeteria, or pick up burgers and picnic in the park. If appropriate, go by and say hello or get acquainted with your spouse's coworkers. Repeat this date for the other spouse's workplace in the not-too-distant future.

3. If you prefer, select one of the date suggestions on page 108 or be creative and customize your own.

EXTRA INNINGS

Complete "Love-Needs Survey" on page 105 and discuss your responses with your spouse.

OPTIONAL NEXT-LEVEL READING

Take your understanding of serving love to the next level by reading some or all of the following.

6 Secrets to a Lasting Love (Tyndale, 2006)
Chapter 5: In Honor of Your Spouse
Chapter 6: Communicating Your Needs

The 5 Love Needs of Men & Women (Tyndale, 2000)
Connecting with Your Wife audio book

SECRET THREE

PERSEVERING LOVE

Persevering love stays strong in tough times and helps spouses feel bonded— best friends for life. You move from giving-up hearts to persevering love.

ROMANS 5:3-4, NIV

WE ALSO REJOICE IN OUR SUFFERINGS, BECAUSE WE KNOW THAT SUFFERING PRODUCES PERSEVERANCE; PERSEVERANCE, CHARACTER; AND CHARACTER, HOPE.

Revealing

SECRET THREE • PERSEVERING LOVE

WARM-UPS
(10 MINUTES)

Read Romans 5:3-4. Thank God for providing strength to persevere through the tough times in marriage. Ask God to develop character and provide strength and hope for the couples in your group who may be facing difficult times right now. Ask Him to prepare you for the future.

In Quads

TEAM BUILDING

Describe a time when you faced a difficult trial in your marriage and tell how God brought you through that time. What did you learn? Think about times like these:

- Severe illness
- Loss of a loved one
- Loss of a job
- Victim of a crime
- Financial crisis
- Extended time of separation
- Victim of a natural disaster
- Job transfer requiring a move
- Overly demanding work schedule
- Wayward child
- Conflict with extended family

Our 6 Secrets Journal

Recall trials you have endured as a couple. Write journal entries for each trial. What did God teach you, and how is He using that after the trial? How is your marriage stronger now that you've been through that experience?

INSTANT REPLAY
(5 MINUTES)

As a Group

1. What have you heard or processed about serving love that hit home or had the greatest impact? Explain.

2. Anyone willing to, describe one way your spouse served you this past week that was especially meaningful, helpful, unexpected, or deeply appreciated. Please elaborate.

3. In what ways do you think the regular application of serving love might positively affect your marriage for good over the long haul?

LEADER: Depending on what is shared, you may want to stop and pray for one another or thank the Lord for what He's been doing in your marriages.

COACHES' COMMENTS
DVD SESSION 4 (22 MINUTES)

Scriptures
Psalm 56:8
Matthew 11:28-30
Psalm 22:3
Isaiah 30:20-21
Romans 5:3-8
James 1:2

OUR WEDDING VOWS

For better or _____

For richer or _____

In sickness or _____

PERSEVERING LOVE

Going through _____ times together

Being _____ together ... best friends

God allowed those times because He needed to

_____ something.

There's a beginning, a middle, and an _____ to every season.

We have a choice. We draw _____
to God. Or we put up a wall, and we run away from God.

We need unconditional _____.

Stay. Just flat-out _____.

God is not _____ with you.

Let those pressures and stresses push you closer to _____.

In case you missed a word during the DVD ...
worse, poorer, health, tough, bonded, refine, end, closer, acceptance, stay, done, Christ

TURN TO YOUR MATE
(5 MINUTES)

Turn to your mate and recall some of the more difficult times through which you and your spouse have persevered. Take a moment to share words of appreciation or encouragement with each other.

LEADER:
For privacy, play some instrumental background music so that couples will not fear being overheard.

DISCUSSING THE DVD MESSAGE
(8 MINUTES)

1. What did Gary or Barb share during the DVD message that was particularly insightful? Discuss.

2. Why do you think vows are part of the marriage-ceremony tradition? Why do you think making a decision to keep your wedding vows is so critical?

3. How do you feel about the fact that God permits trials in your marriage but uses them to refine you, strengthen you, or draw you closer to Him? How do you typically respond during such times?

Understanding

SECRET THREE • PERSEVERING LOVE
(15 MINUTES)

Persevering Love

Persevering love sustains you through the trials of life. As you implement persevering love in your marriage, you will bond with your spouse and enjoy a love that will persevere through your years together.

1. Name some of the couples you know (family, friends, or at church) who have been married 40, 50, or more years. Describe what you admire about their relationship, how they treat each other, or what you know they have endured together.

2. When couples don't persevere but break their marriage vows, they and others suffer consequences. Brainstorm some of the negative consequences you've observed when couples have gone through a divorce. List some below.

Damaged Areas

1. Emotions
2. Spiritual
3. Children
4. Future relationships
5. Finances
6. Others

3. Contrast below the differences between couples who persevere and those who give up.

Persevering   Giving Up

Read Philippians 2:12-13 and answer the questions that follow.

> "My dear friends, as you have *always obeyed*—not only in my presence, but now much more in my absence—*continue to work out your salvation with fear and trembling*, for it is God who works in you to will and to act according to his good purpose."
> **PHILIPPIANS 2:12-13, NIV,** *emphasis added*

4. What do the words *always* and *continue to* obey imply for persevering love?

5. How would you apply "work out your salvation" to the concept of persevering love in your marriage?

6. God helps you want to do His will with regard to your marriage, and He enables you to do it. How do you feel, knowing God wants to help you?

Read 1 Corinthians 13:4-8 and underline the characteristics of love. Then answer the questions that follow.

"Love is patient and kind. Love is not jealous or boastful or proud or rude. Love does not demand its own way. Love is not irritable, and it keeps no record of when it has been wronged. It is never glad about injustice but rejoices whenever the truth wins out. Love never gives up, never loses faith, is always hopeful, and endures through every circumstance.

"Love will last forever."

1 CORINTHIANS 13:4-8

7. If your spouse loved you with the following kinds of love, how would that make you feel? Discuss.

    a. A love that never gives up

    b. A love that never loses faith in me or our marriage

    c. A love that is always hopeful

    d. A love that endures through every circumstance

    e. A love that will last forever

8. Jesus said, "I command you to love each other *in the same way that I love you*. And here is how to measure it—the greatest love is shown when people lay down their lives for their friends" (John 15:12-13, emphasis added). Read the following Scriptures about God's love and make a list in the margin of words or phrases that describe the way we, in turn, should love our spouses.

"He is the faithful God who keeps his covenant for a thousand generations and constantly loves those who love him and obey his commands."
DEUTERONOMY 7:9

God's Example for Our Persevering Love

"How precious is your unfailing love, O God! All humanity finds shelter in the shadow of your wings."
PSALM 36:7

" 'The mountains may depart and the hills disappear, but even then I will remain loyal to you. My covenant of blessing will never be broken,' says the LORD, who has mercy on you."
ISAIAH 54:10

9. In the light of your understanding of persevering love, what changes would you like to make in your behavior, with God's help?

Applying

SECRET THREE • PERSEVERING LOVE

CASE STUDY 1

Sammy and Rosalyn

Sammy is experiencing bouts of depression. He struggles to make it to work each day and is becoming increasingly withdrawn. Rosalyn is trying to support him but struggles to know whether tough or patient love is best.

CASE STUDY 2

Natasha and Peter

Natasha is experiencing infertility and longs to be a mother. Peter is also brokenhearted because he longs to have a child. Natasha wants to discuss adoption, but Peter is having trouble giving up on his desire to have a biological child with Natasha.

CORRESPONDENCE

CASE STUDY 3

Chase and Debra

Chase has lost his job and source of income due to company cutbacks. His job skills are outdated, so he is having trouble finding work. Debra, after being a homemaker for many years, is faced with the necessity of returning to work to keep them afloat.

DISCUSS ONE OR TWO CASE STUDIES (10 MINUTES)

CASE STUDY 1: SAMMY AND ROSALYN

1. What does persevering love look like in this case?

2. What advice or recommended course of action would you give this couple that is consistent with what you've learned about persevering love?

CASE STUDY 2: NATASHA AND PETER

Divide into groups and discuss the following questions. Then share your responses with the large group.

> WIVES: How can Natasha demonstrate persevering love toward Peter as he struggles with giving up on having a biological child?

> HUSBANDS: Suppose Peter has come to you seeking advice. What truths or Scripture might you offer or use to encourage Peter to help him live out persevering love toward Natasha?

CASE STUDY 3: CHASE AND DEBRA

1. What are the struggles, pressures, and emotions Chase and Debra will experience during this trial?

2. Based on what you've learned about persevering love, what would you say to Chase? To Debra? To both?

TURNING TOWARD HOME

Ask whether any couples are facing trying times and would like the group to pray especially for them. If some request prayer, surround them and pray for their needs.

Close by thanking God for His enduring love. Thank Him that He has not left you alone to your own strength or determination. Thank Him for coming alongside to give you perseverance when you need it. Ask Him to give extra endurance and love to prepare each couple for trials that may lie ahead.

Bringing It Home

DATE YOUR MATE

Choose one of the following suggestions and take your mate on a date. After your date, add a memento, picture, receipt, and/or a journal entry to *Our 6 Secrets Journal.*

1. Invite an older Christian couple whose marriage has endured over time to go on a double date with you. This could be parents, in-laws, friends, or a respected couple in your church. Choose a place or an activity that will will allow leisurely talk. Explain what you are studying about persevering love. Ask the couple to tell you stories of some of their trials and how they endured. Ask for their personal secrets to a lasting love.

2. Take a trip to a museum, an art gallery, a historic home, a national monument, or another similar attraction. Enjoy the tour or the sights and reflect on themes of endurance or perseverance that you may observe.

3. If you prefer, select one of the date suggestions on page 108 or be creative and customize your own.

OPTIONAL NEXT-LEVEL READING

Take your understanding of persevering love to the next level by reading some or all of the following.

6 Secrets to a Lasting Love (Tyndale, 2006)
Chapter 7: Love That Endures Tough Times
Chapter 8: Weathering the Storms

SECRET FOUR

GUARDING LOVE

Guarding love protects from threats and helps
spouses feel safe and secure. You move
from unguarded hearts to guarding love.

PROVERBS 4:23, NIV

ABOVE ALL ELSE, GUARD YOUR HEART,
FOR IT IS THE WELLSPRING OF LIFE.

Revealing

SECRET FOUR ● GUARDING LOVE

WARM-UPS
(10 MINUTES)

Read Proverbs 4:23 and ask God to open your eyes to see all the ways your hearts may not be guarded adequately. Pray that those who may have already fallen because of an unguarded heart will be set free, cleansed, and healed.

TEAM BUILDING

By now you should have taken your mate on several dates. Describe the one that's been the most fun, unusual, refreshing, encouraging ... or you choose the word.

OR

If you've been keeping a journal, describe what you have added to your journal besides words.

INSTANT REPLAY
(5 MINUTES)

1. What did you hear or process this past week about persevering love that hit home or had the greatest impact? Explain.

2. What characteristics, attitudes, or actions can contribute most to a love that survives the troubles that confront marriages today?

3. What have you learned about persevering love from observing or talking to couples who have been married for a long time?

LEADER: Depending on what is shared, you may want to stop and pray for one another or thank the Lord for what He's been doing in your marriages.

COACHES' COMMENTS
DVD SESSION 5 (22 MINUTES)

Scriptures

Proverbs 4:23

Philippians 4:7

Often, an _____ heart can set a forest ablaze and put a couple at risk.

Guarding love protects from _____.

so that we can feel _____ and protected.

Men: _____, relationships,

_____ temptation, _____

Women: failure to meet our own _____ needs

We can walk in the power of the _____ of faith around us.

How do you do it?

Stay in the _____.

Stay accountable.

In case you missed a word during the DVD ...

unguarded, threats, safe, work, sexual, passive, personal, shield, Word, confessed, deceptive

Stay _____.

An unguarded heart is a _____ heart.

TURN TO YOUR MATE
(5 MINUTES)

Turn to your mate and describe one area in which you believe you can each step up your guard. Identify one area in which you feel vulnerable and would like to have your spouse's prayer support to help set your guard.

LEADER:
For privacy play some instrumental background music so that couples will not fear being overheard.

DISCUSSING THE DVD MESSAGE
(8 MINUTES)

1. What did Gary or Barb share during the DVD message that was particularly helpful? Discuss.

2. How can a great marriage be put at risk? What are some of the most common threats facing men? Women?

3. What are some things you can specifically do to guard your heart?

Understanding
SECRET FOUR • GUARDING LOVE
(15 MINUTES)

Guarding Love

Guarding love protects your hearts from threats to your marriage. Marriages are threatened by many forces today. If you are not aware of the threats to your marriage, you are vulnerable.

1. Why should a man or woman want to guard his or her heart? Read Proverbs 4:20-23 and describe how important it is.

> "My son pay attention to what I say;
>   listen closely to my words.
> Do not let them out of your sight,
>   keep them within your heart;
> for they are life to those who find them
>   and health to a man's whole body.
> Above all else, guard your heart,
>   for it is the wellspring of life."
> **PROVERBS 4:20-23, NIV**

2. Read the following Scriptures and describe why an unguarded heart is so dangerous to a marriage.

> "If you think you are standing firm, be careful
> that you don't fall!"
> **1 CORINTHIANS 10:12, NIV**

> "Be sober, be vigilant; because your adversary
> the devil walks about like a roaring lion, seeking
> whom he may devour."
> **1 PETER 5:8, NKJV**

3. Read Philippians 2:14-15 and identify characteristics of children of God who have guarded hearts in a culture that doesn't protect marriage.

> "Do everything without complaining or arguing,
> so that you may become blameless and pure,
> children of God without fault in a crooked and
> depraved generation, in which you shine like stars
> in the universe."
> **PHILIPPIANS 2:14-15, NIV**

4. Men, review the list of common threats to a man's heart and discuss the ones that seem to produce the greatest temptations for you. Which threat do you think can most easily sneak up on you and catch you off guard? How can men help hold one another accountable to guard your hearts?

COMMON THREATS TO A MAN'S HEART

a. *Career pressures*—allowing the world's formula for success at work to capture your heart; allowing the demands of a career or job to become more important than relationships with your wife and children

b. *Worldly distractions*—giving inappropriately high priority to pleasure (recreation, hobbies, sports, entertainment, etc.), the pursuit of power or position (seeking influence at work, church, or in the community), or paychecks (pursuing money) over your relationships with Christ and your family

c. *Relationship pressures*—seeking to satisfy the demands and requests of others (boss, church leaders, neighbors, coworkers, community organizations, or friends) to the point that you neglect the needs or desires of your wife and children

d. *Sexual temptation*—yielding to emotional affairs, physical affairs, addiction to pornography, or other sexual sin

e. *The search for significance*—losing all sense of balance in climbing the ladder of success at work, in your career, in finances, in influence, etc.

f. *Passivity*—giving little concern or effort to building and maintaining a healthy marriage relationship

g. *Control*—going all-out to get things your way on your timetable; making unilateral decisions and demanding compliance by others

h. *Competition*—the drive to compete and win in a way that makes others feel like losers

LEADER: Divide into same-gender groups.
- **Husbands, respond to question 4.**
- **Wives, respond to question 5 (p. 66).**

For ways to help guard your wife's heart, turn to page 106.

5. Women, review the list of common threats to a woman's heart and discuss the ones that seem to produce the greatest temptations for you. Which threat do you think can most easily sneak up on you and catch you off guard? How can women help hold one another accountable to guard your hearts?

COMMON THREATS TO A WOMAN'S HEART

a. *Relationships with other men*—yielding to physical or emotional attractions to men other than your husband

b. *Preoccupation with children*—always putting the children's needs first in an unbalanced way that ignores the needs of your husband

c. *Failing to meet personal needs through self-care*—spending so much time and energy meeting the needs of others that you fail to meet your own needs (rest, exercise, time alone with God, time with female friends, etc.) and replenish yourself

d. *Worry*—all-consuming concern for people and circumstances due to a lack of trust in God and His resources

e. *Critical attitude*—tendency to be overly critical, complaining, negative, or nagging toward your husband and children

f. *Comparison*—tendency to find shortcomings or differences in comparison to others and blame others for the shortfall, especially your husband

g. *Control*—going all-out to get things your way on your timetable; making unilateral decisions and demanding compliance by others

For ways to help guard your husband's heart, turn to page 106.

"Let the Lord Jesus Christ take control of you, and don't think of ways to indulge your evil desires."
ROMANS 13:14

6. List ways you can guard your heart and actions that may set you up to "indulge your evil desires," producing an unguarded heart?

    Guarded Heart   Indulge Evil Desires

7. Talk about ways you can build a hedge of protection around your heart and your relationships. For example:
    a. Make and live by a rule not to meet one-on-one with a person of the opposite sex other than your spouse.
    b. Don't share intimately with a person of the opposite sex other than your spouse.
    c. Build a same-sex accountability group that will help you make and keep rules for guarding your heart.

"As iron sharpens iron, a friend sharpens a friend."
Proverbs 27:17

Note:
For additional help in dealing with an exposed, unprotected heart, see page 105.

Applying

SECRET FOUR • GUARDING LOVE

CASE STUDY 1

Jarvis and Jaclyn

Jarvis is oblivious to boundary issues with a woman in his small group at church. Jaclyn senses too much connection, times of flirtation, and Jarvis's preoccupation with the woman.

CASE STUDY 2

Dwight and Mattie

Dwight and Mattie's adolescent child is expressing intense anger toward Mattie. After Mattie experiences a series of verbal onslaughts from the child, Dwight comes home from work and hears her account of another derespectful event.

CORRESPONDENCE

CASE STUDY 3

Hilda and Patrick

After opening a Facebook account, Hilda is tempted to reconnect with an old boyfriend from high school. After honest reflection she realizes that she would expose her heart. That evening she confesses the temptation to her husband, Patrick.

DISCUSS ONE OR TWO CASE STUDIES (10 MINUTES)

CASE STUDY 1: JARVIS AND JACLYN

1. What courses of action can Jaclyn take, and what do you think would be the advantages or consequences of each action?

2. Men, suppose you observed Jarvis's behavior in a small group. How could you respond for the sake of his marriage? What would you say to him? What would you do?

CASE STUDY 2: DWIGHT AND MATTIE

1. What are some possible ways Dwight and Mattie might respond to this threat? Brainstorm possible responses.

2. What are the pros and cons of these possible responses? Which would you recommend for this couple and why?

CASE STUDY 3: HILDA AND PATRICK

1. Based on what you've learned about guarding love, what would you recommend that Hilda do?

2. What can Patrick do to help Hilda guard her heart?

TURNING TOWARD HOME

Use the following Scriptures as part of your closing prayer time.

"Search me, O God, and know my heart;
   test me and know my thoughts.
Point out anything in me that offends you,
   and lead me along the path of everlasting life."
PSALM 139:23-24

"Don't let us yield to temptation, but deliver us from the evil one."
MATTHEW 6:13

Bringing It Home

DATE YOUR MATE

Choose one of the following suggestions and take your mate on a date. After your date, add a memento, picture, receipt, and/or journal entry to *Our 6 Secrets Journal*.

1. Go to the bowling alley, a game room at a family pizza parlor, or another establishment where you can relax and have fun playing games together. Men, forget the competition tonight and just have fun.

2. Double-date with another couple in your *6 Secrets* group. Go to dinner and a movie or another combination of fun and time to talk and get better acquainted. If finances are an issue, invite them over for dinner in your home and play a board game or participate in another fun activity.

EXTRA INNINGS

Review the keys to guarding your spouse's heart on page 106. Identify areas in which you can step up your guard and discuss how you can do that together.

Cut out a picture of a castle from a magazine or print one from the Internet. Put it in a place where you will always see it, such as on your computer at work, in your wallet, on the dashboard, on your refrigerator, or on your bathroom mirror. Use the picture as a constant reminder to guard your marriage castle.

OPTIONAL NEXT-LEVEL READING

Take your understanding of guarding love to the next level by reading some or all of the following.

6 Secrets to a Lasting Love (Tyndale, 2006)
Chapter 9 The Castle of Your Heart
Chapter 10: Building Walls of Protection

Guard Your Heart (Tyndale, 2003)

SECRET FIVE
CELEBRATING LOVE

Celebrating love rejoices in the marriage relationship and helps spouses feel cherished and captivated. You move from isolated hearts to celebrating love.

SONG OF SONGS 1:4; 7:5-6
TAKE ME WITH YOU. COME, LET'S RUN!
BRING ME INTO YOUR BEDROOM ...
[I AM] HELD CAPTIVE IN YOUR QUEENLY TRESSES.
OH, HOW DELIGHTFUL YOU ARE, MY BELOVED;
HOW PLEASANT FOR UTTER DELIGHT!

Revealing

SECRET FIVE • CELEBRATING LOVE

WARM-UPS

(10 MINUTES)

Read Solomon's words in Song of Songs 1:4; 7:5-6. Ask God to renew the joy and intimacy of celebrating love in every marriage.

TEAM BUILDING

Describe one of your favorite celebrations as a couple or family. This could be a single experience that was fun or unusual or a tradition that you enjoy annually. What did you do? Where did you go? Who was there? What happened?

INSTANT REPLAY
(5 MINUTES)

1. What did you hear or process this past week about guarding love that hit home or had the greatest impact? Explain.

In Quads

2. What area did you identify last week that is your greatest threat? What steps are you taking to guard your heart?

3. What, if anything, can we do to help hold you accountable to guard your heart in this area?

LEADER: Depending on what is shared, you may want to stop and pray for one another or thank the Lord for what He's been doing in your marriages.

COACHES' COMMENTS
DVD SESSION 6 (22 MINUTES)

Scriptures

Zephaniah 3:17

Proverbs 5:15-19

We want to enjoy each other. We want to feel cherished, _____.

_____ with God ... we can begin to restore with our mate.

Celebrating love (if we don't put each other on the _____ of the list) can really begin to tarnish.

Wives: Take your calendar and find a _____ night.

Flowers and little gifts can be gimmicks if you are not taking the time to really _____ to each other heart to heart.

Husbands: Your wife loves to listen to what's going on in your _____.

When you bring something onto your plate that will distract you from your family, you've got to ask a question: what are you going to _____ _____?

The greatest gift you can give your children is _____ their father, loving their mother.

In case you missed a word during the DVD ...

captivated, Restoration, top, date, connect, day, take off, loving, relationships, emotional, three

Cultivate healthy _____ outside your marriage.

It's so important to maintain that connection. That's the _____-intimacy part of celebrating love.

Spiritual intimacy: it's when you have a relationship of _____ (husband, wife, and Christ).

74

TURN TO YOUR MATE
(5 MINUTES)

Turn to your mate and reminisce about your favorite moment of celebrating love in your marriage so far. What could you do to recapture a similar joy through celebrating love? Wife? Husband?

LEADER:
For privacy play some instrumental background music so that couples will not fear being overheard.

DISCUSSING THE DVD MESSAGE
(5 MINUTES)

1. What did Gary or Barb share during the DVD message that increased your desire to experience celebrating love with your spouse? Discuss.

2. What suggestion did you hear that you realize will create a better environment for you to experience celebrating love with your spouse?

3. How does spiritual intimacy contribute to your relationship, causing celebrating love to grow stronger and deeper?

Understanding

SECRET FIVE • CELEBRATING LOVE
(18 MINUTES)

Celebrating Love

Celebrating love equips you to maintain a satisfying emotional, physical, and spiritual connection. Celebrating love keeps that spark alive, not only in the bedroom but in all areas of the relationship. As you learn to celebrate your oneness, you will fall in love all over again.

1. Read below about God's celebrating love for you. How do you feel to know He loves you like that?

   "The LORD ... is a mighty savior. He will rejoice over you with great gladness. With his love, he will calm all your fears. He will exult over you by singing a happy song."
   ZEPHANIAH 3:17

2. List 5 to 10 things you love about your spouse. Then share with your group and your spouse two things you love about him or her.

3. Read Paul's words below and describe one reason you can rejoice and be glad about the love you and your spouse share in Christ.

   "As you hold out the word of life—in order that I may boast on the day of Christ that I did not run or labor for nothing. But even if I am being poured out like a drink offering on the sacrifice and service coming from your faith, I am glad and rejoice with all of you. So you too should be glad and rejoice with me."
   PHILIPPIANS 2:16-18, NIV

4. Discuss how each of the following five keys to celebrating love can enhance your joy and love for one another.

In Quads

FIVE KEYS TO CELEBRATING LOVE

1. PUT EACH OTHER AT THE TOP OF THE LIST
- You need quantity time before you can enjoy real quality time.
- Put family second, right after your relationship with God.
- Be cautious when making commitments outside your family.
- Cultivate enriching relationships.
- Make communication a priority in your relationships.
- Let your body language demonstrate that your spouse is your priority.

2. CONFESS TO EACH OTHER
Close the loop; see pages 101–3.

3. GET TO KNOW EACH OTHER AGAIN

4. RETHINK YOUR THINKING
- Be willing to fall in love with your spouse again.
- Control your thoughts.

5. REKINDLE ROMANCE AND PHYSICAL INTIMACY
See Proverbs 5:18-20.

Proverbs 5:18-20

"Let your wife be a fountain of blessing for you. Rejoice in the wife of your youth. She is a loving doe, a graceful deer. Let her breasts satisfy you always. May you always be captivated by her love. Why be captivated, my son, with an immoral woman, or embrace the breasts of an adulterous woman?"

5. Using the five keys, share as many ways as you can think of to celebrate your love for your spouse.

For more ideas on how you can celebrate your spouse, see pages 106–7.

As a Group

Ecclesiastes 4:12
"A person standing alone can be attacked and defeated, but two can stand back-to-back and conquer. Three are even better, for a triple-braided cord is not easily broken."

6. Read Ecclesiastes 4:12 in the margin. Why is spiritual intimacy between you your spouse a vital part of a Christian marriage? What is the benefit of having Jesus as the third strand?

7. How can spiritual intimacy help you have—

   • grace to show forgiving love?

   • humility to show serving love?

   • patience to show persevering love?

   • wisdom to show guarding love?

   • joy to show celebrating love?

   • power to show renewing love?

8. What kinds of activities and attitudes could be roadblocks to a couple's spiritual intimacy?

9. Why do you think spiritual intimacy in marriage can be so hard to maintain?

10. What kinds of activities and attitudes do you think characterize couples with strong spiritual intimacy?

Applying

SECRET FIVE • CELEBRATING LOVE

CASE STUDY 1

Dimitri and Nikki

Dimitri and Nikki are in the busy years, with children in elementary school. They catch themselves coming and going, with an absence of times to connect and talk. There's very little romance or celebration in their marriage.

CASE STUDY 2

Katlyn and Brian

Katlyn grew up in a vibrant Christian home watching her dad lovingly serve her mother spiritually. Brian grew up in a home that did not walk with Christ. When they move to another city, Brian opts not to look for a new church. Katlyn is losing her joy, speaking less of spiritual matters, and withdrawing. During a phone call with his previous accountability partner, Brian concludes that he has caused a spiritual dry season not only for himself but also for his wife.

CORRESPONDENCE

CASE STUDY 3

Lori and Derek

Lori is not having her emotional and spiritual needs met, so she finds herself both actively avoiding sexual intimacy and alone time with her husband, Derek. After several times of rejection, he stops initiating lovemaking, leaving her feeling insecure and absent of his pursuit.

DISCUSS ONE OR TWO CASE STUDIES (10 MINUTES)

CASE STUDY 1: DIMITRI AND NIKKI

What advice would you give Dimitri and Nikki to help them rebuild their emotional, spiritual, and physical intimacy so that their celebrating love will flow once again?

CASE STUDY 2: KATLYN AND BRIAN

Husbands, suppose you are Brian's accountability partners. What would you recommend that he do to begin rebuilding the couple's spiritual intimacy?

Wives, suppose you were Katlyn's best friends before her move, and you just found out about her present lack of spiritual intimacy. Regardless of whether Brian comes around, what would you recommend that Katlyn do? What can you do as friends to encourage her?

CASE STUDY 3: LORI AND DEREK

Divide into two groups and answer the following questions. Then share your responses with the larger group.

> WIVES: What can Lori do to start rebuilding celebrating love in her marriage? What can she change about her responses to Derek that might help?

> HUSBANDS: What does Derek need to do to rebuild emotional and spiritual intimacy with Lori? Review the list of ways to celebrate your wife on page 106 and select a few suggestions for Derek to start celebrating his wife.

TURNING TOWARD HOME

Pray one-sentence prayers thanking God for His love and asking Him to foster emotional, spiritual, and physical intimacy among the couples in your group so that you can experience celebrating love in the full measure He desires for you.

Bringing It Home

DATE YOUR MATE

Choose one of the following suggestions and take your mate on a date. After your date, add a memento, picture, receipt, and/or journal entry to *Our 6 Secrets Journal*.

1. Review the ideas for celebrating your spouse on pages 106–7 and start practicing them this week. Plan a romantic dinner. Make a list of reasons you love your spouse. Share them over dinner and let the sparks fly if God is stirring your hearts.

2. Now may be the time to pull out all the stops and go on a romantic getaway. Go to a bed-and-breakfast, chalet, or special resort for a special time of celebration. Tell your spouse all the reasons you love him or her that you wrote on page 76, number 2.

3. Enlist your kids (if you have them) to help create a romantic evening at home. Decorate with flowers and candles. Ask the kids to serve your dinner in front of the TV and watch a great romantic movie.

4. If you prefer, select one of the date suggestions on page 108 or be creative and customize your own.

OPTIONAL NEXT-LEVEL READING

Take your understanding of celebrating love to the next level by reading some or all of the following.

6 Secrets to a Lasting Love (Tyndale, 2006)
Chapter 2: Rekindle the Joy of Being Married
Chapter 12: Building Spiritual Intimacy

The 5 Sex Needs of Men & Women
(video series, LifeWay Press, 2007)

The 5 Sex Needs of Men & Women
(Tyndale, 2006)

40 Unforgettable Dates with Your Mate
(Tyndale, 2002)

SECRET SIX
RENEWING LOVE

*Renewing love refreshes and supports
the marriage bond and helps spouses
feel confident and rooted. You move
from stuck hearts to renewing love.*

MALACHI 2:15
DIDN'T THE LORD MAKE YOU ONE WITH YOUR WIFE?
IN BODY AND SPIRIT YOU ARE HIS. AND WHAT DOES HE
WANT? GODLY CHILDREN FROM YOUR UNION. SO GUARD
YOURSELF; REMAIN LOYAL TO THE WIFE OF YOUR YOUTH.

Revealing

SECRET SIX • RENEWING LOVE

WARM-UPS
(10 MINUTES)

Read Malachi 2:15. Thank God for what He has been doing in your marriages over the past seven weeks of this study. Ask Him to give wisdom, strength, and a renewed commitment to each couple to divorce-proof their marriage and pursue their dream with the six kinds of love.

TEAM BUILDING
Share with the group the one thing you have learned or experienced during this study that has most impacted your life and your marriage.

INSTANT REPLAY
(5 MINUTES)

1. What did you hear or process this past week about celebrating love that hit home or had the greatest impact? Explain.

2. Share one of your favorite experiences on dates with your mate.

3. Of all the secrets we've studied, which one has had the greatest impact on you and how?

LEADER: Depending on what is shared, you may want to stop and pray for one another or thank the Lord for what He's been doing in your marriages.

COACHES' COMMENTS
DVD SESSION 7 (25 MINUTES)

Scriptures

Joshua 24:15

John 3:16

John 15:5

John 13:17

Renewing love refreshes and supports the marriage bond and helps spouses feel _____ and rooted.

It's not the quality of your circumstances that defines your marriage. It's the quality of your _____.

It's for the sake of the next _____.

OUR COVENANT HOME

1. You initiate a _____ love when you offend each other or conflict arises.

2. You demonstrate _____ love by putting each other's needs above your own.

3. You exercise _____ love by walking through difficult times—hand in hand.

4. Establish a _____ love that will safeguard our marriage and let no man, woman, or child divide us.

5. Enjoy a _____ love that keeps the spark alive in the relationship and celebrates you as my best friend.

6. Experience a _____ love that says, "I'm committed to you until death do us part."

In case you missed a word during the DVD ...

confident, relationship, generation, forgiving, serving, persevering, guarding, celebrating, renewing, marriage, Christ, body, encouragement, stay, ego

You cannot un-one your _____.

It starts with committing to _____.

You need the local _____ of Christ.

CHEERLEADERS

1. Their _____ can turn a game around.
2. They stay in the game. They _____ to the end.

Get your _____ out of the way and choose God.

TURN TO YOUR MATE
(5 MINUTES)

Turn to your mate and discuss your responses to the following questions.

1. What will you do to build the various kinds of divorce-proofing love into your marriage? List three things.

2. Which kind of love do you most need today to begin divorce-proofing your marriage?

3. Where are you and your spouse going to concentrate your efforts right now?

LEADER:
For privacy play some instrumental background music so that couples will not fear being overheard.

Kinds of Divorce-Proofing Love
- Forgiving Love
- Serving Love
- Persevering Love
- Guarding Love
- Celebrating Love
- Renewing Love

DISCUSSING THE DVD MESSAGE
(10 MINUTES)

1. What did Gary or Barb share during the DVD message that was particularly insightful or instructive? Discuss.

2. What are some ways or areas in which spouses can be cheerleaders for each other? List some ways.

3. What are some ways the body of Christ can better root for and encourage marriages and families? List some ways.

4. What couples do you know who might benefit from the study of *6 Secrets to a Lasting Love?* Discuss ways you, your group, or your church can help other couples pursue their dream marriages and divorce-proof their marriages.

Understanding

SECRET SIX • RENEWING LOVE
(10 MINUTES)

Renewing Love

Renewing love regards the marriage covenant as unbreakable. Renewing love protects you from insecurity and provides you with confident assurance as you face the future with your spouse.

1. Read the Scriptures below and discuss why a renewing love that commits to a permanent marriage is so important for God's people.

> "You cry out, 'Why has the LORD abandoned us?' I'll tell you why! Because the LORD witnessed the vows you and your wife made to each other on your wedding day when you were young. But you have been disloyal to her, though she remained your faithful companion, the wife of your marriage vows. Didn't the LORD make you one with your wife? In body and spirit you are his. And what does he want? Godly children from your union. So guard yourself; remain loyal to the wife of your youth. 'For I hate divorce!' says the LORD, the God of Israel."
> **MALACHI 2:14-16**

> "When you make a promise to God, don't delay in following through, for God takes no pleasure in fools. Keep all the promises you make to him. It is better to say nothing than to promise something that you don't follow through on. In such cases, your mouth is making you sin. And don't defend yourself by telling the Temple messenger that the promise you made was a mistake. That would make God angry, and he might wipe out everything you have achieved."
> **ECCLESIASTES 5:4-6**

2. What difference will it make in your marriage if you both make a decision that divorce is not an option, that you will keep your covenant promise? That promise may have been along the lines of—
   - for better or worse;
   - for richer or poorer;
   - in sickness and in health;
   - to love and to cherish;
   - till death do us part.

3. Read the descriptions of renewing love in the box below. How would you define *renewing love* in your own words?

Renewing love is ... _____

_____

_____

_____

RENEWING LOVE—
- provides an environment in which the deepest level of human trust can form;
- supplies the security that allows intimacy to fully develop;
- protects you and your spouse from the fear of broken promises;
- helps you rediscover the roots of your relationship and stay vitally attached to the love of your life;
- provides security for the children raised in your home;
- undergirds all the other loves and allows them to flourish.

4. The real heart of renewing love is the commitment to keep growing together. What does that mean? How can spouses grow together? List as many ideas as you can.

5. Do you truly believe that wherever you might be on the Marriage Map today, you can still realize or achieve the dream?

❙ Yes   ❙ No   ❙ I'm afraid to hope.

6. Look at the list below and check the loves you believe will most effectively bring the growth your marriage needs now. Then indicate in the blank to the right which love you believe deserves the highest priority in your strategy to get back or continue on the road to the dream. Identify your top three priorities.

	Priority
❙ Forgiving love	_____
❙ Serving love	_____
❙ Persevering love	_____
❙ Guarding love	_____
❙ Celebrating love	_____
❙ Renewing love	_____

Read the following Scripture as a final instruction from the Lord for the kind of love for each other that lasts.

"Rejoice in the Lord always. I will say it again: Rejoice! Let your gentleness be evident to all. The Lord is near. Do not be anxious about anything, but in everything, by prayer and petition, with thanksgiving, present your requests to God. And the peace of God, which transcends all understanding, will guard your hearts and your minds in Christ Jesus. Finally, brothers, whatever is true, whatever is noble, whatever is right, whatever is pure, whatever is lovely, whatever is admirable—if anything is excellent or praiseworthy—think about such things. Whatever you have learned or received or heard from me, or seen in me—put it into practice. And the God of peace will be with you."

PHILIPPIANS 4:4-9, NIV

THE PLAN OF SALVATION

As Gary shared how he came to faith in Christ, you may have recognized that you need Him too. Truly, without Him you can't love your spouse in the ways we recommend in this study. He can enable you to love in a whole new dimension. The way you can experience Christ as Savior is as simple as ABC.

A. Admit to God that you are a sinner: "All have sinned and fall short of the glory of God" (Rom. 3:23, HCSB). Agree that you need a Savior.

B. Believe in Jesus Christ as God's Son and receive Jesus' gift of forgiveness from sin. In the death of Jesus on the cross, God provided salvation for all who would repent of their sins and believe in Jesus: "God loved the world in this way: He gave His one and only Son, so that everyone who believes in Him will not perish but have eternal life" (John 3:16, HCSB).

C. Confess to others your faith in Jesus Christ as Savior and Lord. Share your decision with your spouse, your group, and your pastor. Ask for baptism as a public expression of your faith and become part of a local church. If you need more help, talk to a Christian friend or a pastor.

Applying

SECRET SIX • RENEWING LOVE

CASE STUDY 1

Oscar and Maurene

Oscar and Maurene are in the midlife years, losing their joy and feeling disconnected. In the early years they were child-focused; but now, as the children have left the nest, they find themselves facing each other, feeling like strangers, and considering divorce.

CASE STUDY 2

Zach and Helen

Zach and Helen are newlyweds. In the first year of marriage they realize just how different their interests are. Zach loves to ski the slopes; Helen loves to lie on the beach. He loves a good game on TV; she loves to cruise the malls. He is passionate about working out at the gym; she loves to hang out with her girlfriends over coffee.

CORRESPONDENCE

CASE STUDY 3

Melissa and Michael

Melissa and her husband, Michael, have recently given their lives to Christ. They had made many mistakes in their marriage prior to this decision and were close to divorce. Now they are ready to begin a new life together, with Christ at the center of their marriage.

DISCUSS ONE OR TWO CASE STUDIES (10 MINUTES)

CASE STUDY 1: OSCAR AND MAURENE

What specific recommendations would you make for actions Oscar and Maurene can take to renew their love for one another?

1. Husbands: How would you counsel Oscar?

2. Wives: How would you counsel Maurene?

CASE STUDY 2: ZACH AND HELEN

1. Husbands: Suppose Helen approaches you for some big-brother advice about how she can step into Zach's world. What are some suggestions you would offer to her?

2. Wives: Suppose you are good friends with Zach. He confesses that he just doesn't understand women. He asks for some big-sister advice on how to connect with Helen. What would you suggest that he do?

CASE STUDY 3: MELISSA AND MICHAEL

Based on what you've learned about the six secrets to a lasting love, what practical steps would you recommend for this couple as they make a fresh start in their marriage?

TURNING TOWARD HOME

Turn to "Our Covenant Home" on page 109 or use the display copies you may have ordered from the Rosbergs. Read the covenant together and invite couples to renew their covenant with each other by signing their copies.

Invite couples to join hands. Thank God for all He has done to enrich and strengthen your marriages. Acknowledge that you are entering fresh covenants with Him and each other to have great marriages till death do you part.

Invite volunteers to respond to God in prayer also.

Bringing It Home

DATE YOUR MATE

Take a fresh assessment of where you are on the Marriage Map (pp. 95–100) prior to your date. Have you made progress in moving toward your dream marriage? Prepare to talk about areas of strength and weakness in your marriage. Commit to keep pursuing the dream.

Take your mate on a date. (You don't have to quit having dates just because your group study is finished.) Plan an extended time in which you can talk about your experiences over the past seven weeks. Discuss where you are on the Marriage Map and what you want to do in the days ahead to pursue your dream marriage. After your date, add a memento, picture, receipt, and/or journal entry to *Our 6 Secrets Journal*.

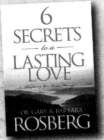

OPTIONAL NEXT-LEVEL READING

Take your understanding of renewing love to the next level by reading some or all of the following.

6 Secrets to a Lasting Love (Tyndale, 2006)
Chapter 13: A Love That Is Fresh Day After Day
Chapter 14: Nurturing a Lifetime Marriage

Renewing Your Love (devotional, Tyndale, 2003)

The Great Marriage Q & A Book (Tyndale, 2006)

EXTRA INNINGS

THE MARRIAGE MAP
FOR USE AFTER SESSIONS 1 AND 7

For each stop on the Marriage Map, we've compiled a list of indicators that may help you determine where you are in your marriage. First work through the assessment alone, checking any indicators that describe the *current state* of your marriage. Be honest and transparent. Don't check what you want to be true; check reality.

Although you may check your responses on the following pages, we recommend for privacy that each spouse use separate paper for recording responses. You have permission to photocopy this section for your personal use. This will also allow you to use this map on other occasions to measure the growth of your marriage. You may want to jot down a note to elaborate on why you checked a particular indicator. After both you and your spouse have completed the assessment, we will guide you to discuss your responses and try to honestly identify where you are in your marriage. Rest easy; we will not ask you to share these responses in your group.

You will probably identify some indicators in many of the stops. Keep in mind that your responses will often differ from those of your spouse. That's because you are evaluating your behavior or that of your spouse, and he or she is looking at the other side of the relationship from his or her own perspective. Each of your perceptions will be important in helping you get a realistic view of your relationship.

Before you begin, pray and ask God to guide you as you respond. Ask Him to shine light on your marriage and to help you see what He sees. Ask Him even now to begin increasing your love for your spouse. Pledge to Him your desire and willingness to begin moving toward your dream marriage, regardless of where you and your spouse find yourselves on the map.

On the following pages or on separate paper, check all the indicators that describe the current state of your marriage. If you are not sure how to respond or have a question, write a note to bring this up when you discuss your responses with your spouse.

For a more detailed description of the stops on the Marriage Map, read chapter 2 in the trade book *6 Secrets to a Lasting Love* (see p. 112).

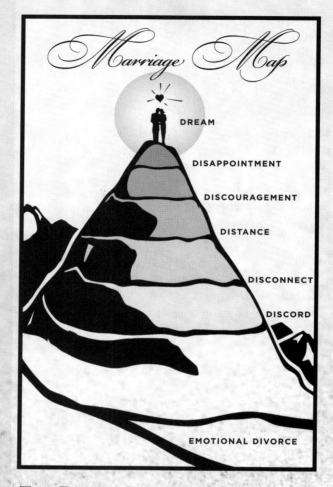

THE DREAM STOP

H W

☐ ☐ 1. I communicate freely with my spouse, and we keep
   no inappropriate secrets.

☐ ☐ 2. I forgive my spouse when I am wronged and seek forgiveness
   when I offend. I am loved without strings.

☐ ☐ 3. My spouse and I eagerly seek to discover and meet each
   other's needs.

☐ ☐ 4. We have faced and conquered difficult circumstances that
   have undone other marriages.

☐ ☐ 5. I consciously guard myself against threats and temptations
   that could pull our marriage apart.

☐ ☐ 6. We enjoy ongoing emotional, physical, and spiritual closeness.

☐ ☐ 7. We are committed to keeping our relationship fresh and alive
   "till death do us part."

THE DISAPPOINTMENT STOP

H W

☐ ☐ 1. I have difficulty expressing affirmation to or about my spouse.

☐ ☐ 2. My spouse isn't the flawless person I thought I married.

☐ ☐ 3. I feel surprised and let down when I notice an imperfection in my spouse.

☐ ☐ 4. My spouse and I have caused each other to feel hurt and angry.

☐ ☐ 5. My spouse and I have experienced conflict over personality differences, male/female wiring, or ways of doing things we learned from our families.

☐ ☐ 6. I compare my spouse to other people.

☐ ☐ 7. I have a mental list of things I wish I could change about my spouse.

THE DISCOURAGEMENT STOP

H W

☐ ☐ 1. I often wonder whether I am missing out on something in my marriage.

☐ ☐ 2. I have a mental list of reasons I am dissatisfied with my marriage.

☐ ☐ 3. My spouse implies or says I don't understand him or her or know how to meet his or her needs.

☐ ☐ 4. My own needs are not being met in my marriage. I feel as if my spouse's friends, work, church involvement, and/or the kids are more important than I am.

☐ ☐ 5. Even when I recognize my spouse's needs, I am not successful at meeting them.

☐ ☐ 6. I have a difficult time expressing my needs in a way my spouse can understand and act on.

☐ ☐ 7. I wonder whether my choice of a spouse was a mistake.

THE DISTANCE STOP

H W

☐ ☐ 1. I could describe our relationship as "fair to partly cloudy, with no clearing in sight."

☐ ☐ 2. I often fill my free time with activities that don't include my spouse.

☐ ☐ 3. I have given up most of my expectations of my spouse.

☐ ☐ 4. I wonder whether my spouse ever feels excited about being married to me.

☐ ☐ 5. My spouse sometimes seems like a stranger to me.

☐ ☐ 6. I keep many of my thoughts and feelings from my spouse.

☐ ☐ 7. I worry that we might someday face a problem bigger than our resolve to stay together.

THE DISCONNECT STOP

H W

☐ ☐ 1. I sometimes feel lonely even when I'm with my spouse.

☐ ☐ 2. It is difficult for me to feel that my spouse loves me. I may know it intellectually, but I don't sense an emotional connection.

☐ ☐ 3. When we are together, we seldom have much to say to each other.

☐ ☐ 4. When we talk to each other, we often misunderstand and misinterpret each other.

☐ ☐ 5. I prefer to devote my time, energy, and money to something or someone other than my spouse.

☐ ☐ 6. I doubt that my marriage can grow or change for the better.

☐ ☐ 7. I don't think my spouse is very interested in who I am or what I want to do.

THE DISCORD STOP

H W

☐ ☐ 1. Most of my thoughts about my spouse are negative.

☐ ☐ 2. My spouse and I verbally lash out at each other, saying things that are hurtful.

☐ ☐ 3. I often wonder what it would be like not to be married or to be married to a different person.

☐ ☐ 4. I daydream or fantasize about another person who would make a better spouse.

☐ ☐ 5. I feel as if my spouse and I are at war.

☐ ☐ 6. True tenderness with my spouse is a faded memory. We avoid sexual intimacy.

☐ ☐ 7. Family and close friends notice that our marriage is severely strained.

THE EMOTIONAL-DIVORCE STOP

H W

☐ ☐ 1. I am staying married for some reason other than love for my spouse.

☐ ☐ 2. I have given up hope that my marriage could be better.

☐ ☐ 3. I pretend I'm OK with my marriage to keep up appearances.

☐ ☐ 4. My first goal in my marriage is to protect myself from further pain.

☐ ☐ 5. My spouse and I have separated or have considered separating.

☐ ☐ 6. My heart is deeply attached to someone other than my spouse, even if I am not acting on that feeling.

☐ ☐ 7. I know I have already walked away from my marriage emotionally.

You have permission to photocopy this assessment for your personal use.

REVIEWING WHERE YOU ARE ON THE MARRIAGE MAP

Once you've completed your assessment, get together with your spouse and discuss your responses, one stop at a time. Add your spouse's responses to your sheets. Discuss your perceptions, which probably differ in places. If you added notes to clarify a response, share those also. Observe your places of agreement. Carefully listen to the differences. This is not a time to argue but to listen.

After the two of you have shared your responses for each stop, review what you have checked and answer the following questions.

1. Which of the stops seems to more nearly describe the current state of your marriage? Why do you think so?

   Husband's perception:

   Wife's perception:

2. Do you see your marriage in the same place, or do you differ in your assessment?

3. What have you learned about your marriage in this process?

4. In light of this insight, what do you want to do about your marriage?

Ask God to help you be willing to work on your marriage to move toward His plans for your life together. You are not in this effort alone. God is present and working. We're going to coach you over the coming weeks. And your small-group members are going to help one another. We're going after great marriages together!

CLOSING THE LOOP

FOR USE AFTER SESSION 2

A PATTERN THAT PRODUCES PAIN

1. *The offense.* It all starts when one spouse offends the other in some way.
2. *The hurt.* Just as a physical wound brings pain, relational offenses traumatize our emotions. They hurt, some much more than others.
3. *The anger.* When hurt is not addressed, anger develops; and anger often prevents conflicts from being resolved peacefully. God never said, "Don't be angry." He said, "In your anger do not sin" (Eph. 4:26, NIV). Anger itself is not sin, but inappropriately handling anger may lead to sin—hurtful words, bitterness, or violence.

Hurt can cause anger. But sometimes anger can be sparked by one person or event and can be taken out on someone else. Anger can also arise from a past experience that may not even be remembered.

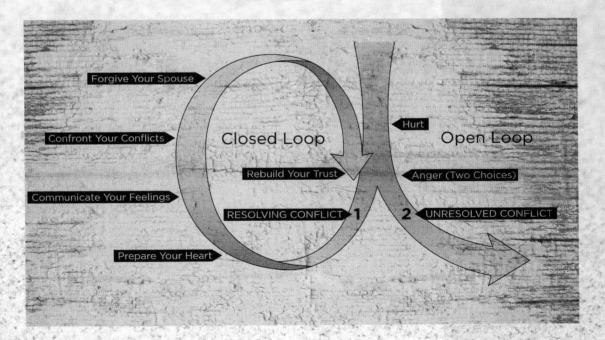

For more help on closing the loop, see *Healing the Hurt in Your Marriage* (Tyndale, 2004).

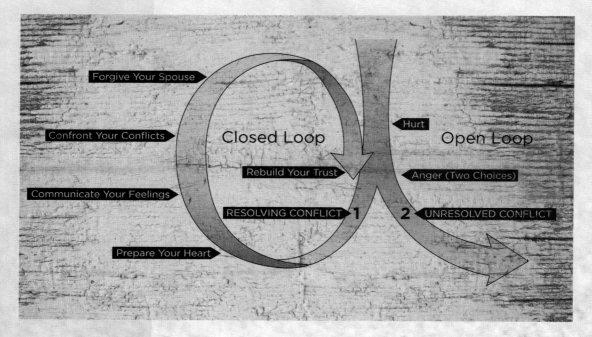

Forgive Your Spouse

Confront Your Conflicts

Closed Loop

Hurt

Open Loop

Rebuild Your Trust

Anger (Two Choices)

Communicate Your Feelings

RESOLVING CONFLICT **1**

2 UNRESOLVED CONFLICT

Prepare Your Heart

RESPONDING TO THE PATTERN THAT PRODUCES PAIN

Choice 1: Ignore the offense and hurt, allowing the anger to fester. You may continue to stuff your unresolved feelings deep inside, resulting in bitterness, resentment, and depression. You may explode, venting pent-up anger without regard for how it wounds and alienates your spouse.

Choice 2: Resolve the conflict through forgiving love. When you face hurt and anger, you can decide to resolve the conflict. That's the biblical way to deal with the offense-hurt-anger pattern. As individuals and as couples, we want to work toward a commitment to address the pain and anger, to resolve the conflicts, to forgive the offender, and to renew the relationship. The goal is to bring the relationship to a place of healing, wholeness, and openness, helping you feel accepted and connected again.

Make a commitment to address the unresolved conflicts in your marriage. Begin following these steps to resolve conflicts and demonstrate forgiving love.

Step 1: Prepare Your Heart
- Humble yourself and pray. Prayer softens our hearts.
- Look for the underlying cause of the conflict.
- Commit to making your relationship the top priority.
- Involve a trusted accountability partner.

Step 2: Communicate Your Feelings
- Think ahead about what you want to say.
- Recognize gender differences in communication.
- Get a referee. When the issues are too big or too painful to deal with on your own, find an objective, trustworthy third party to help you talk them out.
- Deliver your whole message. Speak kindly and calmly, but say all you have come to say.
- Commit to listening.
- Focus on the positive. Affirm positive traits or habits.
- Avoid the silent treatment.
- Say what you mean.
- Don't use generalizations.
- Use I messages instead of you messages.
- Agree on a plan for handling conflicts.

Step 3: Confront Your Conflicts
- Choose an appropriate time and setting.
- Ask permission to address the conflict.
- Avoid statements that assign blame.

Step 4: Forgive Your Spouse
Whole forgiveness requires two persons—one seeking forgiveness and one granting it—and the heartfelt statements described below.
    Requesting forgiveness:
1. Confession: "I was wrong."
2. Sorrow: "I'm sorry."
3. Repentance: "I don't ever want to hurt you like this again."
4. Request: "Will you forgive me?"
    Granting forgiveness:
1. "I forgive you and close the loop on this issue."
2. "I forgive you for ..."

Step 5: Rebuild Your Trust
When the wounds are deep and trust has been eroded, rebuilding trust is essential. If you have deeply or repeatedly hurt your spouse, he or she may be willing to forgive you. But that doesn't mean the relationship is completely healed. For true restoration to occur, you must work to rebuild your spouse's trust over a period of time. Prove to your spouse over the long haul that your confession, contrition, and repentance are genuine.

EXAMPLES AND OPPOSITES OF FORGIVING LOVE

FOR USE AFTER SESSION 2

Read again our definition of *forgiving love* in the margin on page 27. Below are more examples of forgiving love and examples of being stuck in unforgiveness.

EXAMPLES OF FORGIVING LOVE

- Accepting forgiveness but being patient when your spouse needs time for trust to be restored or hurts to be healed
- Confessing you were wrong and asking for forgiveness
- Praying for God's blessing and forgiveness of the offender
- Making restitution for your offense
- Taking action to demonstrate your love and restore intimacy in your relationship
- Expressing forgiveness and never bringing up the matter again
- Refusing to be offended
- Taking the initiative to reconcile the relationship when you are the offender

EXAMPLES OF BEING STUCK IN UNFORGIVENESS

- Refusing to grant forgiveness because the offense was too serious
- Describing your spouse's latest mistake during dinner with your in-laws
- Allowing feelings of guilt and shame to shut down communication
- Pouting and keeping your distance
- Getting children or others to take your side to force a confession
- Refusing to talk about the problem or the offense before forgiveness has taken place
- Taking action to get even or making sure your spouse pays a price for the offense
- Staying busy with other activities to avoid having to spend time with an offending spouse

LOVE-NEEDS SURVEY
FOR USE AFTER SESSION 3

On a separate sheet of paper or in *Our 6 Secrets Journal* (or below if you prefer) rank the following love needs, based on their importance to you. One (1) would be most important, and 20 would be least important. After both spouses have completed their surveys, plan a time to discuss your lists. Focus attention on the top 5 or 10. Be curious. Ask your spouse how you could contribute to meeting specific needs.

H	W		H	W	
____	____	Admiration	____	____	Romance
____	____	Career support	____	____	Security and stability
____	____	Communication and emotional intimacy	____	____	Sexual intimacy
			____	____	Significance
____	____	Companionship	____	____	Spiritual intimacy
____	____	Domestic support	____	____	To be desired
____	____	Encouragement and affirmation	____	____	To provide and protect
			____	____	Trust
____	____	Family relationships	____	____	Unconditional love and acceptance
____	____	Honesty and openness			
____	____	Nonsexual touch	____	____	Understanding and empathy
____	____	Personal time			

For more details, see *The 5 Love Needs of Men & Women* (Tyndale, 2000).

ACTIONS FOR DEALING WITH AN EXPOSED, UNPROTECTED HEART
FOR USE AFTER SESSION 5

1. Confide in a close and trusted Christian friend to help you fight this enemy of your marriage.
2. Share your struggle with your spouse and fight this threat together.
3. Decide today to adopt God's guarding love and defeat this threat. It is never too late to start guarding your heart.
4. Spend more time in prayer and the study of God's Word to gain confidence that God will fight for you. Your heart needs to be encouraged that His love is more powerful than any threat to your marriage.
5. Decide not to give up. God's love can provide a way to defeat the threat; and He can give your marriage a fresh, new start!

GUARDING YOUR SPOUSE'S HEART

FOR USE AFTER SESSION 5

KEYS TO GUARDING YOUR HUSBAND'S HEART

Wives: Read the following seven ways you can help guard
your husband's heart.

1. Honor him and his world.
2. Avoid sabotage by yielding your need to be in charge.
3. Love him unconditionally.
4. Understand and respect your gender differences.
5. Honor his friendships.
6. Clarify your family roles.
7. Commit yourself to him and to God.

KEYS TO GUARDING YOUR WIFE'S HEART

Husbands: Read the following seven ways you can help guard
your wife's heart.

1. Listen!
2. Offer practical help.
3. Make time just for your wife.
4. Give her time for herself.
5. Love her unconditionally.
6. Demonstrate spiritual leadership.
7. Pray for and with your wife.

For more help, see *Guard Your Heart* (Tyndale, 2003).

IDEAS FOR CELEBRATING LOVE

FOR USE AFTER SESSION 6

IDEAS FOR CELEBRATING YOUR HUSBAND

1. Send him off and welcome him home with a smile and a kiss.
2. Let him know you're glad he's home just because you love him, not
   because the sink is clogged or you need to get away from the kids.
3. If you arrive home after your husband does, find him before you
   do anything else and tell him how glad you are to be home.
4. Let him know you care. Buy a mushy card and send it to his office,
   hide it in his briefcase, or slip it into the book he's reading at bedtime.
5. Write down a list of reasons you love him; then share the list with him
   over a romantic dinner.
6. Leave him a surprise note with an encouraging Bible verse.

7. Buy attractive new nightwear for yourself—and hide his!
8. Give him massages.
9. Pray for him before he leaves for work.
10. Join him in his favorite activity even if you aren't crazy about it. Try doing with him some of the things he enjoys doing with his buddies.
11. Say, "I'm sorry" when you are wrong and forgive him when he is wrong.
12. Initiate sexual intimacy.
13. Listen to his opinions on spiritual issues. Ask him what types of activities would fuel his spiritual growth. Don't impose your ideas on him.
14. Leave him a voice-mail message saying you love him and are praying for him.
15. Eat breakfast with him and enter his world at the start of the day.
16. Accept your body and enjoy experimenting with him sexually.

IDEAS FOR CELEBRATING YOUR WIFE

1. Be accessible to her—always! Tell her where you will be and how long you will be gone.
2. Let your coworkers know you can always be interrupted when she calls.
3. Repeat your wedding vows often. Tell her that if you had it to do all over again, you would choose her again—and again and again.
4. Continually promise and reassure her that your love for her and faithfulness to her are "till death do us part."
5. Invite her to tell you how she desires to be loved; then seek to love her in that way.
6. Give her a head-to-toe massage.
7. Compliment her, especially for the little things.
8. Send flowers, chocolates, or whatever little gifts she likes.
9. Attend a marriage conference together. Take the initiative to locate one and make all the arrangements, including a babysitter if needed.
10. Lavish her with nonsexual touch.
11. Call her during the day just to say hello.
12. Put your arm around her or hold her hand in public.
13. Say, "I love you" before she does. Begin and end each day with encouraging words.
14. Regularly write notes to her telling her how proud you are of her.
15. Hold her hands and pray for her.
16. Send her cards or love letters.
17. Bring her breakfast in bed.

For more help, see *The 5 Love Needs of Men & Women* (Tyndale, 2000).

DATES WITH YOUR MATE

We've recommended dates with your mate each week in the "Bringing It Home" segment of the session. Some of these suggestions relate to the content of the week. For other dates you may want to choose from the suggestions below or customize your own. Be creative and have fun. Plan ahead to get the most out of your time together. Rekindle the romance!

1. *Love letters.* Plan an evening at home. Pull out and read some of your old love letters or cards. Rekindle the emotion. Review some of your dreams.

2. *Marriage markers.* Plan for a time to identify and list the key events in your marriage that marked significant directions, transitions, accomplishments, or happenings. Record the list in *Our 6 Secrets Journal.* How have you seen God's hand in directing you through the years? Take time to thank Him. Share some of these markers with your children.

3. *Count your blessings.* Go for a stroll together in your neighborhood, at a park, or on a hiking trail. Take turns naming the blessings you've received from the Lord. Be specific in naming people, events, provisions, surprises, protection, and so forth. Use conversational prayer to thank God for these blessings.

4. *Music night.* Order pizza or another favorite for dinner at home. Pull out records, tapes, CDs, or music videos of music that was popular when you were dating. Play your favorites and share the memories. Sing along.

5. *Road trip.* Go on an all-day road trip to visit neighboring towns. Start the day at a coffee shop. Have lunch at a unique restaurant or picnic in a park. Visit interesting shops, historic places, or an antiques mall. Take the scenic route on your drive and talk about some of your favorite trips or vacations. Capture some photos along the way.

6. *Your chick and a flick.* Husbands, take your wife to the video-rental store and ask her to select her favorite movie of all time. Get snacks and cuddle for an evening at the movies.

7. *Sports fans.* Wives, take your husband to a game, race, or another favorite sporting event. Settle for a TV event if necessary. Be a fan for a day.

If you need more ideas for that unforgettable date, get a copy of *40 Unforgettable Dates with Your Mate.* Saying, "I do" doesn't mean you're done! The Rosbergs share ideas on how you can bring the zing back into your marriage. This book gives you everything you need to plan fun dates to meet your spouse's needs. The best parts of the resource for you may be the dozens of questions that will stimulate and guide conversations with your mate. (See p. 112.)

OUR COVENANT HOME

Together as husband and wife, we declare our home a divorce-proofed home—a covenant home—built on the solid foundation of Jesus Christ, characterized by unconditional love, and devoted to our lifelong commitment to each other.

By signing this covenant, we promise to—
- initiate forgiving love when we've offended each other or when conflict arises;
- demonstrate serving love by putting each other's needs above our own;
- exercise persevering love by walking through the most difficult times—hand in hand;
- establish a guarding love that safeguards our marriage and lets no man, woman, or child divide us;
- enjoy celebrating love that keeps the spark alive in the relationship and celebrates you as my best friend;
- experience a renewing love that says, "I'm committed to you until death do us part."

In the presence of God and these witnesses and by a holy covenant,
we promise to exhibit these loves toward each other every day.
We promise to do so from this day forward, for better,
for worse, for richer, for poorer, in sickness and in health,
forsaking all others as long as we both shall live.

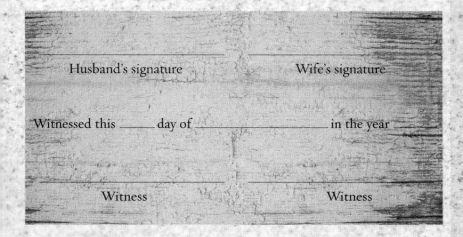

_____   _____
Husband's signature   Wife's signature

Witnessed this _____ day of _____ in the year _____

_____   _____
Witness   Witness

To order a color, printed version suitable for framing, see number 3 on page 110.

SMALL-GROUP LEADER SUGGESTIONS

Thanks for volunteering to facilitate this small-group experience of
6 Secrets to a Lasting Love. We've designed this study to make your job relatively
easy and enjoyable. You'll notice that the session plans in this member
book provide a listening and discussion guide for use with the DVD
segments, questions and activities to guide Bible study and develop an
understanding of the 6 secrets, and case studies to help your group apply
the secrets to real-life situations. Let's take a look at your role as leader.

1. *Set a time and place for your group meeting.* Choose a home or another
   informal setting. Allow at least 75 minutes for each session. Enlist a
   host couple to attend to the details. Include a TV and DVD player.

2. *Enlist participants.* Limit your group to no more than six couples to
   maximize sharing and enhance closer relationships among members.
   If you have more people interested, enlist other leaders and form
   additional groups.

3. *Secure resources.* You'll need a leader kit with the DVDs for yourself.
   Order member books for each couple (or each individual if preferred).
   You may want to make available copies of *6 Secrets to a Lasting Love* trade
   book by Tyndale so that couples can go deeper in study and application.
   The leader kit includes a sample copy for your review. Consider ordering
   color display copies of "Our Covenant Home" (p. 109) for use in the
   final session at *www.drgaryandbarb.com.* Allow three weeks for delivery.
   These can also be used in a marriage-renewal service at your church.

4. *Preview the session plans* each week and select the questions and activities
   you believe will be most interesting and helpful to your group. You will
   not likely have time for all the suggestions, so pace yourself. We've
   given suggested time frames for each segment. If you have more than
   75 minutes for your session, you can expand those times.

5. *Become familiar with additional resources.* Visit *www.thegreatmarriageexperience.
   com* and *www.lifeway.com/marriage* to identify additional resources (print,
   recorded, radio, and events) that may benefit your members.

6. *Prepare for a referral.* Contact your pastor or another trusted Christian
   leader and ask for suggestions if a couple needs a referral to a Christian
   counselor. Let your group know you have this information if they
   decide they need additional help.

7. *Prayerfully guide the sessions.* Pray and trust the Lord to be present and
   working in people's lives as you guide the sessions. Watch for times
   you may need to pause and invite the group to pray for an individual
   or a couple. Talk and pray with others after the session if needed.